the slotted spoon

by jennifer faus

also by
Jennifer Faus

BACKCOUNTRY
BEFORE SUNDAY
THE DEVIL'S MECHANIC
THE DISSENTER
IVAN & ME
RATHLIN
SHE

Published by Koser Howe Publishing LLC

Printed and bound in the United States of America
ISBN# 978-0-9854710-7-1

Cover design: Chris Parks
chrisparks.me

thank you

Steve
friendship

WILEM
my reason

Glen
steadfast belief

Tony & Frances
shelter & grace

Jerry
one of the good guys

Shawn & Jennifer
kindness & generosity

Nancy
linen & cheer

Kim
strength & conviction

Willis
ham & beans
cornbread & fellowship

Carole
guidance & truth

Blake
indomitable spirit

Chris
beauty & broth

Jordan
presence & afternoon movies

Paul
hero & mentor

you are offended by my joy
that isn't going to stop it
like the waves at ballycastle
it just keeps rushing in

poem for an october day

as the car rolled off the highway
she thought
that's probably the winning lottery ticket in my wallet
because that's the way things go for me
and she recalled
how she thought that on an october day
like today
she would lie in the meadow
above the greys river road
under the blue sky dotted with white
and finish what those two women started
the two women who resented her birth
the first because she had to give her up
the second because she had to take her
a mental inventory
no epiphany
it didn't matter if it happened or not
if it had to happen
this was a good time
a good place

after the fire

the hawk
glides and soars
his work unobstructed by needles and cones

the landscape
changed
lush forest to desert plants

the ponderosas
burned black with soot
stand

a testament to doing what you were born to do
no matter the hardship
no matter the cost

simply
if you are a tree
stand

marriage

he climbed though the second story window
in the middle of the night
the window at the back of the house
the neighbors less likely to notice
the hour of his return

he held her head down
her face pressed against the pillow
forcibly penetrated her
telling her it was her duty
her duty to submit

a lifetime ago
she still finds it hard to say
my husband raped me
she can still smell the alcohol and the women
the sex of other women on him

she still feels the shame
and confusion
between crying out for him to stop
and believing
it was her duty

indecision

and so it came to pass
that I was not
as I had thought
a Soldier for the Lord
but a maiden in the master's house
conscripted to his bidding

* * * *

and so it came to pass
that I was not
as I had thought
a Soldier for the Lord
but a maiden in the master's house
indentured to his bidding

homeless

I want to collect fall leaves
yellow red orange brown
and press them
between sheets of waxed paper
the iron on low

I want to set the table for supper
turkey stuffing potatoes peas
lay china on a linen cloth
pressed smooth and stiff
the iron on high

I want to prepare the guest room
curtains eiderdown pillows vase
arrange stems of berries
place them on the table
the old iron bed

I want to light candles on the mantle
silver white purple gold
arrange tinsel on the tree
turn over the wood in the hearth
the antique iron poker

I want to open my arms
son daughter grandchild friend
as the children run-up the steps
family laden with packages
the wrought-iron gate

I want to make chili
bake cornbread
and serve it bubbling and crisp
the cast iron skillet she gave me
knowing my love for Lodge pans

I want the life before him
before the abuse
the blood loss
before the iron poured out of my body
draining vitality—life

I want release from these iron bars
to be free to walk in the woods
to collect autumn's abundance
yellow red orange brown
to press between sheets of waxed paper

kansas

my fingers are in the sun and they are hot
they hold my paper against the wind
the line demarcating shade and sun
crosses the midpoint of my hand
like so many midwestern storms
the stiff gridded structure of the midwest
so dictatorial
rain marches across the plains in bands
so strict
he can stand on his porch in the sun
watching hail pour down upon his barnyard
round pebbled pieces to be collected by children
to ice down watermelon
to drop down the sides of the ice cream maker
while familiar legends of survival
tornadoes | blizzards
drown out familial truths
infidelity | abuse
the difference in temperature is dramatic
the fingers of my hands in the sun
the backs of my hands shaded

building wealth

she thought
there were those

who had been without money
for so long

that for them
it ceased to have meaning

she didn't want to contemplate the hardships
endured on the road to that end

mills canyon two

we walked at six a.m. to avoid the heat
out to the grove of cottonwood trees
past the pear tree
untended from 1904
still bearing fruit
by nine a.m. he had his hole dug under the stone
to wait out the hottest part of the day
nine a.m. <> five p.m.
I sat low in my chair
my arms and neck and head covered
wool blankets
antithetical to 105 degrees
necessary as I leaned over my work
my hands and face exposed

we are so accustomed to following the rules
he and I
being told where to go
what to do
when to stand—to sit
how to pray ̄
that it never occurred to us to pack our belongings
and move to the shade of the cottonwood grove
to wait out the hottest part of the day
we are so accustomed to following the rules
he and I
that it never occurred to us to pack our belongings
and flee

and our skin browned
and reddened like the sandstone
of the walls
of the canyon

and our faces lined
and roughed like the sandstone
of the walls
of the canyon

with the wind and the sun
of New Mexico

my father is dead

every morning he wakes me at 5 am
get up!
get going!
if you want success you've got to get up!
and I do

I have children to get to school
an employer to please
I ride 20 miles
I hit the heavy bag
I do yoga

nothing prepared me for Him
I was busy being happy and satisfied with my life
I wasn't paying attention
my father wakes me everyday at 5 am
until Him
and then he chucks it in and is gone

my father is gone
he could never stick out the tough stuff
or maybe
he couldn't bear to watch it
to witness me giving my life away

he shouted get up!
get going!
why didn't he shout
GET OUT!

the corner store

we sat
two people together
on the curb of a sunny steamy afternoon
and she said
I can still walk into the bank and withdraw $20

it's coming
it is coming
the time is soon coming
when that will no longer be possible

she asked me for a cigarette
I took one for myself then handed her the pack
she said, you can't afford that
it's all I have left, I told her
then turned my face to the heavens and gave thanks

6 p.m. 4-car train

the brown line is running 8 car trains
a rate of 3 to 1 to the green line
three 8-car trains brown
one 4-car train green

brown line people stretch out in their shining
retrofitted cars with their lattes and new york times

the green line car I'm in smells like a goat—no lattes
we're too packed in to enjoy hot beverages or to read
I can however count the pulse and respirations of the
person in front of me

good practice for the EMT classes I take at night
2 jobs, 4 kids, college: a nice break in my 20-hour day

the faces of the brown line women
look like snow white: botox, collagen, full time nanny
brown line people look clean well-rested carefree
at the end of the day

six a.m. 4-car train
six p.m. 4-car train

the faces of the green line women
show the tyranny of worry and distress
unanswered prayers
cries of injustice etched on their foreheads

the agony of loss of unrealized dreams rides along
pressed against your back your front

green line pain is visceral
still
on the green line no one is alone
there is company in poverty

one night
the doors opened on the wrong side

the night fell away below us
us up on the elevated track
the gentle embrace of a young gangster
kept me from falling out of the car

the brown line patron would have let me drop
there is no company in wealth

economizing my time
I ride from library & van buren
to adams & wabash
in the the spacious sterile environs of the brown line

polished aluminum reflects the light
of the newly installed overhead lighting system

I see my tired reflection in the windexed windows
the sterile windexed people so clean so transparent
but for the sniveling disdain
you wouldn't know they were there

Bukowski didn't have to deal with this shit
<or, the soul-sucking life of blogging>

What if ... I wrote my fucking memoir.

What if ... I sold everything and fucked off to _____. I'm not saying where. If I actually did it five other people would know and my secret would be out.

What if ... I went to the store and got a pack of cigarettes and an orange.

What if … I had a normal size fridge, in a kitchen that didn't have a giant hole in the floor, that had a range with an oven door that closed, in a house that was my own.

What if ... I just wrote to Liam explaining myself.

What if ... all those years, I'd spent that time building something of my own.

What if ... I won the lottery. I could build Waldorf schools and give kids free tuition to attend them.

What if ... I folded the laundry.

What if...I wrote Deering or Estes and what if that lawyer who told me he knows something told me what he knows before he dies. Would it be something? Or nothing.

What if ... I hadn't believed him every time he lied?

What if ... I found a writer-director relationship?

What if ... I figured out how to utilize blogging more effectively?

What if ... I moved the aloe from the front of the house to the side and put the half-dead half-alive Bougainvillea in it's place?

What if ... I quit whining and sat at my desk and wrote something, anything, because that is the only way these things get done.

What if ... I got a fucking "real" job and quit this shit.

Ugh. I don't feel like writing today.

It is on these days that old bastard Bukowski comes round spurting that goddamn sonnet about air and light and time and space, telling me,

"no baby, if you're going to create ...
you're going to create..."*

and then calls me a cunt or a whore, drinks that awful tequila, and vomits on my carpet.

"How else would you know it's me?" he retorts. "It's all about persona these days. Except everyone wants to be so goddamn likable. Unlikeable worked for me. Sticking with it. Gotta smoke?"

And like Bukowski, I doll out two.

And so I will write today. Even if it is only because Bukowski shamed me into it.

* * *   (Thank you E.B. White, for the asterisk)

I don't feel like writing today.
But I will.
Because that is how it works.
But, what if….

PTSD: trauma

There are hints to my condition.
The hollow darkened places that frame my eyes.
The chipped polish on my nails.
The unhealed cut on the top of my hand.
Overgrown hair, thinning at the ends.
A small tear in my sleeve.
A ragged cuff, a missing button.
All indicia I gave pieces of myself away.

PTSD: war

The Army doesn't tell you when you get on the plane
that when you land in Afghanistan
you have to unzip your soul
and pour it on to the ground.
It is impossible to retrieve something lost
among so many grains of sand.

PTSD: daily

Periods of angst.
Periods of calm confidence.
Periods of anger resentment.
PTSD.

we all make choices

You chose it.

People like to say this to me.

As if they think I got what I deserved because
I chose it.

Yes. I chose it.
I believed a guy who lied to me.
Lied to me every day.
He lied.
I believed him.
He lied.
I believed him and I followed him
like Jim Jones followers
followed him
to their deaths.

They chose it.

People say it to me all the time.
Whenever it—the subject of abuse—comes up.
You chose it.

So I got what I deserved
for believing a liar
a fraud
a practiced psychopath.

Jim Jones followers.
Got what they deserved?

They chose it.

Those people that died in that plane crash
chose to get on that plane.
They got what they deserved?

They didn't know the pilot was depressed.

I didn't know he was a psychopath.

But you stayed.

A woman being beaten stays after the first beating.
She deserved the second?

She chose it.

And if she doesn't get out after the second beating?
Deserved the third?

She stayed.

So?

Sure.

After all.
We all make choices.

mutual admiration

My Grandmother and I admired each other.
I wanted to be more white gloves.
She wanted to be more barefoot.

footnote

it is better to die white gloves
than barefoot

The Slotted Spoon

She will give you a slotted spoon for your broth and if you question her decision she will tell you–you are spoiled, ungrateful.

She will say that even though you and she have had your difficulties, she has always loved you.

If you complain of hunger she will tell everyone what a difficult child you are, what a difficult child you have always been, how hard it has been for her, how she has suffered. But for this child, my life would have been....

And when you say, she gave me a slotted spoon to eat my broth, she cries out, I would never do such a thing! and they comfort her and tell her, of course, we know you would never do such a thing, and whisper among themselves, what a retched child.

And she whispers: She's always angry.

She says this about you and then, for proof, refers back to the time she gave you a single chopstick to eat your steak and you were frustrated.

And they will see, by this example, that she is a truth teller.

That you have always been angry.

They say, yes, we see what you mean, and pat her arm
and feel for her because she has been burdened with
a difficult, nay—an unreasonable child.

Mother, I cannot eat my broth.
You are ungrateful. You are always complaining.
May I have a different spoon?
Other children are happy with what they have. Why
are you always unhappy?
Perhaps I could have peas. I can eat peas with the
slotted spoon.
You are always so negative.
I can't finish the broth.
You've always been a quitter.

So you pick up the bowl and drink the broth.
And now.
You are different.

See? She has never been like us. I've never
understood her.

And they nod and say, yes, we see what you mean.

companions

I don't need to hike across the country
to hear the voices of my dead
I don't need to walk 1000 miles
to chase my demons
they are sitting right here next to me
gathered round my table
there's a fucking 18% tip added
whenever I go out for a meal

*"You gonna go up to the gas-station, buy a pack of
cigarettes, then hang out on the corner and
smoke with the crack-heads?"*

at 36

She drinks scotch. Neat.
She forgets to shave.
She dips and falls and ebbs and flows.
She loves you tremendously.
She loves you hard.
She bares her breasts and arms, belly and back.
Her raw, untamed, unrelenting soul wraps around.
She forces her heart into yours.
You haltingly accept.
Then, suddenly, from nowhere, she'll want it back.
She'll plunge her fist into your chest, wrap her fingers
around her heart and rip it out through your sternum.
You're devastated. (But)
You knew you never really wanted it in the first place.

dead men

sitting in a coffee shop
police wander around across the street
a fire truck pulls up
they arrived for the loan of a ladder
the cops are searching for a gun
the gun used to shoot a man dead on his porch
the firemen (it's all men)
prop up the ladder and hold it while a fat man
wearing a pale blue polo shirt, dark blue pants, and
sky blue rubber gloves struggles to the top
he gazes out over the roof
it does not appear he intends to climb from the
ladder onto the roof to search for the gun
he does not
his gaze must be sharp

driving to the library
pulled to the side of the street
for a funeral procession
people still do that here
pull over and wait for the dead and his mourners
to pass
there are six cars in his procession
accompanied by four escort vehicles
(all driven by men)
we wait, he passes, we proceed

watching TV
two firetrucks pull up in front of the house
one first-response
one ladder-truck
I stand and cross to the door
not this house, one of the men signals to his
(male) colleague, "it's the one next door!"
the husband has had a heart attack
he was dead before he hit the kitchen floor
his cigar rolled under the stove
the cigar continued smoking, hence the ladder-truck
the firefighters stay
30-40-50 minutes
long after the cigar is extinguished
long after the ambulance collected the husband
to be taken
to be pronounced
by the proper authorities

all of these dead men and none of them him

the apartment behind the oak grove

I remember a dance
dancing around chanting
chanting "I want to go home"
I don't know if I said anything else but I know I said
"I want to go home" over and over as I danced
more like—moved laterally through space
as if by so doing I could slip through time
across an ocean to another continent
I am unsure whether this was before or after
time is liquid
my memory is—standing in the street on the Strand
I don't know how I got from the Oak to the Strand
I was standing there on the Strand with a suitcase
and boxes at my feet and a car came
and I don't remember if it was the IRA taxi
or Ivan's Mercedes
there was before that moment
and there was that moment
I don't remember the in-between
I know I was in Derry
because my notes—the dates on my notes
I must have been there after
for some period of time after
I wrote about this time as if I remember it clearly
I wrote about it based on my notes
I must have been there before and after
I was chanting "I want to go home"
I feel like I haven't found my way
I'm still trying to get home

the coast guard

at half nine this morning I noticed him
I watched him reading a book on the beach
ball cap, rain jacket, fitted slacks, hiking boots
all normal in appearance
the condition of his beard gave him away
I knew his story

at four p.m. he noticed me
walking along the boardwalk
I was eating a stick of bread
he looked at me hard and intentionally
he held my gaze to let me know
he knew my story too

a wednesday morning in july

He said, "I'm not spying on you, I'm looking out the window."

I said, "I know. I know what you are looking at. It's OK."

"My friend was killed last night." He indicates the dozen police cars, the yellow crime scene tape, the news van.

"I'm sorry."

"It was about three a.m. He was sitting on the porch drinking and this guy came up. I guess he spilled a drink and the guy went in to get something to clean it and he came back with a gun and shot him in the chest."

"The shooter—he lived there?"

"No."

I wait.

"He was a meth-dealer. He was there visiting his cousin. Some guy named Felix."

"The shooter. Do they have him in custody?"

"Yes, but they can't find the gun. That's what they are doing. Looking for the gun."

He looks down. He hesitates. He can't seem to decide whether to go out the door of the coffee shop or stay in. I am unclear as to who is who. Who is the cousin? Who is the meth-dealer? Who lives where? Who shot who? I don't seek clarification. I reach for him instead. I hug him. And he hugs me back. He cries. He doesn't let go. I tell him, "you are going to be OK." He grips me tighter and I respond.

Two strangers. Arms wrapped around each other in the doorway of a coffee shop.

"Thank you," he says. He steps back, turns, and walks out the door. He walks away and then returns to sit at the cafe table adjacent to the window where I am working. I consider closing my laptop and going out to sit with him. Just to be with him so he is not alone. But I don't. Among all the empty tables, he sat at that table. Perhaps that is close enough for him. To feel not alone.

I worked for a while, then packed my belongings and left. I walked down the alley behind the coffee shop. I am always noticing how overgrown it is. It seems like a good place to dump a gun. Maybe if I can find the gun, he will feel reassured. A police car pulls up and I point out to the officer some clothes stashed in a bush. "Looks like they've been there a long time," he says. From the way he says it, it is clear. I've interrupted him.

Me. A woman in heels, pencil skirt, starched white shirt, a briefcase slung over her shoulder, digging though wet leaves and mud, looking for a gun. Trying to help. The officer returns to his car, gets in, and drives off, leaving me standing in the overgrown alley. Feeling foolish.

Seattle Public Library

tall
black
man
a black bandana covers his face

Washington Laws
two books on the laws of Washington
one propped up
he is copying the contents
typing the words into the computer
that is what he appears to be doing

three large black bags are stacked behind him
one duffle
two backpacks
his home?

I wonder about him
but I wonder about everyone
he sits erect—firm
angry?
driven?
unapproachable

and so, I, and now you, will not know his answers
his story
in spite of his silence I don't imagine when he goes
it will be quietly

predictive text

they say the past is the best predictor of the future
if her past is a landscape of washed out bridges
if today is a stain of failure
how does she have hope
for the future

ladies who lunch

The short-haired blonde has a long skinny nose.
It dips into her coffee cup with every sip.
She has no knowledge of current events.
She carries a flask in her handbag.
She has been married for 40 years.

The red suited one wears mismatched accessories.
Zuni earrings with a Mainliner pearl choker.
She smokes like a chimney.
Barks orders like a drill sergeant.
She's buried two husbands.
Her boyfriend just rang.
He is on his way to collect her.

There is a wrinkled PhD sitting next to me.
She has sparkling eyes and bad breath.
She knows everything and shares her knowledge.
She narrates the entire event for us.
The Universe spins around her as she flits up & down.
Up and down, up and down, in and out of her seat.
She works the room while her daughter attends her.
Her husband died six months ago.
She's engaged.

A long-lashed, silky-tressed girl sits across from me.
She has an engaging smile and large hungry eyes.
Her clothes are impeccable.
Her face is flawless.
She engages in quiet conversation with the guests.

She is witty and kind, soft and sweet.
I would do anything to sit next to her.
To hold her hand.
To feel her laughter.
She is single.
She will be alone for the rest of her life.

Justice is at home among the elite and well traveled.

sloppy joe and the brackish farmer

Hemingway's death
informs us about what it is to be a writer.

The death of Hemingway
informs us about what it is to be a writer.

The way Hemingway died
informs us about what it is to be a writer.

Hemingway dying
informs us about what it is to be a writer.

The suicide of Hemingway
informs us about what it is to be a writer.

Hemingway killing himself
informs us about what it is to be a writer.

When Hemingway died,
we were informed about what it is to be a writer.

Someone else wrote that.
Or something like that.
I don't recall the exact words.

Presently it seems we are consumed with the way to write. We're lectured on being conservative. Our sentences should be conservatively constructed.

(But.) It wasn't because of the structure of the sentence that I remember it. It wasn't the order of the words or the words chosen or the perfected grammar. The writer might have written "it gives us a glimpse into what it is to be a writer," but I don't remember because it wasn't the technical specificity that stayed with me. It was the resonance.

The professor replies, "conservative construction allowed the sentence to resonate."

But | While | And still

E.B. White wrote about sand on the floor of his beach house and we were captivated.

neither a gold watch nor a plaque

she told the untold stories
the stories
of heroes
of victims
of ordinary people
she put the sound, the resonance, the song
to the voices that go unheard
it was her desire to tell untold stories
this desire led her to chicago where
she told stories of kids who lived in public housing
to kansas where
she pled celia's case and told the story of prig v pa
to northern ireland where
she told the stories of the bloody sunday victims
to wyoming where
she told the story of a female veteran living with ptsd
today she retires
like the school janitor
before school janitors were unionized
then outsourced
when it was just one guy sweeping up trash
with one exception, one difference
where someone asked,
 "what ever happened to Mr. Russell?"
no one will ask after her

Crosspurpose

Do you feel it?
Something's missing.
The sex is great.
The conversation? Polite.
There. That's it. I think I hit it.
You are polite and considerate and that is good.
But you are hiding something. So it doesn't quite fit.
I'm no yin to your yang.
No one would pick us out of a crowd as a couple.
Is it good?
You say it is good for us to ease into this relationship.
Maybe I would believe that it is good for us to ease
into this relationship—evolving into a couple slowly,
over time, with friendship as a foundation if you didn't
fall in so easily with my friend.
It would be better, our gradual relationship would be
better, if you didn't fall in so easily with my friend.
You laugh at her jokes, engage her in banter, party
with her until dawn.
You yin her yang.
Oh well.
Chatty men who share your secrets and dance til
dawn are a dime a dozen.
It's great sex that's hard to find.

Rogers Park

I wish it would rain all night.
The steady heat has broken.
The sky opened and it just came falling in
over the sill onto the floor
splattering my files of nothing.
Bills, utilities, tax returns. Nothing.

The night ones are out.
Hootin 'n hollerin in the twilight.
They are laughing.
They are talking.
Loudly.
It could be mistaken for (by the untrained ear)
but it is not
fighting.

The rain has soaked in before the liquor.
This time.
The thunder dims their anger.
The downpour drives them indoors.
Quiet.
Just the sound of the rain.
For now.

in tribute

Why did you kill him?

He left the toilet seat up.

In the morning, when he left for work—up
After dinner—up
In the middle of the night—up
Saturday afternoon—up
Watching football—up
After taking a shit while reading a magazine—up
At the strip club—up
At his girlfriend's—up
After picking up cocaine—up
At the track, the card game, the fight—up

Those goddamn toilet seats were up all over town.

Not anymore.

frequent flyer

He asked me
Just before he left again
For months
Again
If I was still writing

I quit drinking
I quit smoking
I joined corporate
I am in a re-la-tion-ship
How could I be writing?

dreams

when I was with him
I used to have dreams
I frequently had dreams about being attacked
and not being able to scream
I tried to scream
but no sound came out
since I left him?
not once

the absence of hope

I'm an emotional girl
I have big defined muscles
but I am fragile

I can sit in a room and not shower
Not eat not breathe
Just write
For writings sake

Fuck Bukowski
He wrote everything worth writing
He ruined it for the rest of us
Who also experience life

Life is not so different from human to human
The pain is the same
Million dollar pain
Food stamp pain

That bitch
Anne Frank
Made us believe there is good in everyone
She's a fucking liar

It takes too much effort to be good
The bad in everyone
That's easy

for the masses

she died
floating in a plastic pool
a copy of Strunk and White
balancing on her chest
(the masses can google Strunk and White)
this is for the writers who know

* * *

she died
floating in a plastic pool
the little book
perched precariously on her chest

Strunk would have struck precariously
Strunk would have struck precariously
Strunk would have struck precariously

but White would let it in

The NYC subway in "You've got mail" had a butterfly.
Ours has yellow jackets.

How are you today?
Are you benevolent?
Did she suck your cock and you fell asleep?
Did she ride you hard and you washed the truck?
Did she bare her soul and you watched the game?
How many bruises did you make today?
How many steps are there to the Lincoln memorial?

Did you notice POW-MIA black and white and think
"Crazy old fucks. They look alive & well to me."

You are beautiful, he said
I love it when you do that
You make me feel sooooooo good
You are amazing
You make me hard
You make me cum
You make me feel like a man
You are so beautiful

Beauty fades in the company of seamen
Dries out your skin and makes your throat raw
How many times
How many men
What was she thinking
What was he drinking

Two empty glasses
One cup of hot tea
Four small children
One bed
One paycheck
No net

One park-bench
One sadness
One harvest moon
One, "Taxi!"

I've got to get a cab
I suppose I should get a cab
Where's that damn cab
I've been waiting on that cab
I am waiting for a fucking cab

I've got people
People need me
Did you call a cab?

She closes the door

The purple, blue, and yellow contours on her
arms, legs, and back

heal

Friday–Sugarite State Park

To town to check email
egg sandwich add green chilis and coffee
no text messages
seven emails
five job rejections
one job request
a $50 job for which I will have to play 20 questions
with the paralegal to get the information I need to
write the motion
I'll do it Monday
one invitation to a President's Circle event

The weekend warriors arrived
among them a dozen women on a weekend retreat
I tried to give away my too-small Vasque hiking boots
these women don't need used boots
I tossed them in the trash
maybe I could have sold them
but they do have that cat-pee history
so maybe, I thought, it's better not to be greedy

Windy today
not just windy, blustery
wind wind wind wind
left windows open to air out the Jeep
now everything is covered in dust

Duke is hunting a chipmunk
so we go

up and down and
up and down and
up and down
the nature trail

On the way to town there was a story on the radio
about people in Japan phoning their dead relatives
from a phone booth, a particular phone booth a man
set up to talk to his deceased brother
I feel angry at some of my dead relatives
I'd like to give them an earful

Yesterday I talked to The Universe:
I feel ready to move on to the next chapter in my life
I am ready to start the next chapter in my life

maybe The Universe disagrees
maybe The Universe is apathetic
maybe The Universe doesn't give a shit
maybe The Universe doesn't exist
and is, after all, just
the universe

one page from Proust

distracted by the wind today
temperature set at or about body temperature
just enough to let you know it is there
not enough either way to warm you or to cool you
a southern wind
more than a breeze less than a blow or a gale
though none here would call a wind a gale
I am sitting at the park villa next to the pond where
we used to try to catch tadpoles
the pond was fenced then and it was difficult even
with the slender arms of childhood to reach through
to the water and scoop out the tiny frogs-to-be
the wind catches wisps of my hair
I let it down so the collective strands can benefit
jocular freedom:
how I imagine my hair would feel about being let
down to play with the wind
individual strands tumble over one another
each strand letting the wind carry it away from my
shoulders and back again
throwing itself down each time in a different pose like
sculpture tag
the game we played as children after the sun
dropped below the horizon but before the fireflies
appeared while the sky held enough light to catch
our angular bodies frozen in tortured art
there is a scent of flowers
not a heady perfume just enough to let me know
there are flowers nearby

bees passing under the shade of the pavilion provide
affirmation
other than that the air is unusually free from the odors
of this city which range from jet fuel to silage—this city
where one third of the economy is dependent on
farm fish and forestry
there is no fence now
they've removed the fence that surrounded the pond
this means that anyone could in theory or in practice
simply step into the water but they've sealed off the
rocket-ship slide so no one can climb up and look out
over the park and imagine traveling beyond the
horizon and then climb down and slip down the
metal slide to the ground
my cynical nature responds—the holes were cut for
1950s sized people you climbed a short ladder up
through a hole to a landing then walked around the
landing to climb another short ladder up through a
hole and so on four or five transitions to the top
from this perspective everyone on the ground looked
small you could see the zoo's seals lying on rocks
sunning lost in their dreams—probably of the sea—
while a short jaunt away the river beckoned telling
you that you could build a boat and sail away
even the stars were in reach and if you were lucky and
your mother brought you to the park in the cool
evening of a hot July back when July was hot your
place above the street lamps meant you could see
the stars and at the top of the rocket-ship they
weren't just for imagining
twenty-first century sized people aren't likely to fit

through those holes I speculate it was decided:
better to seal them up than face another lawsuit from
an injured obese person or navigate an ADA claim
so you can't reach for the moon from this place
anymore
it is safer now
they say the rocket-ship had become dangerous
it is not a town of dreamers
nor for dreamers
(nor Dreamers, if one is so inclined)
it is not a place to fancy another kind of life
so it was best to seal the holes before another
generation of children climbed to the top and
dreamed themselves away
there is no fence around the pond now just a
prohibition which no doubt someone—very likely a
best-selling author—produced and the city manager
thought was clever stating:
wild animals may swim
but wild people may (only) watch
the (only) being implied of course
clever maybe perverse even kinky if considered
but no words against scooping tadpoles
perhaps only because no one has attempted that
activity or rather no one has yet been caught
attempting it for if you caught a tadpole and
observed its transformation
you might find yourself inspired
to dream

for hire

I am neither an artist nor a scholar.
I am a journeyman.
Pay me and I will write what you ask.
I will do it to your specifications, on time, and
within budget.
I am recently thinking I might be well-suited
to job of assassin.
I do not get lonely.
I prefer to work alone.
I am outcome oriented.
I do not go to the office to make friends.
Perhaps if I had done a more careful reading of *What
Color is Your Parachute* when my father gave it to me
(his response to my desire to have a conversation
with him about what I might do with my life) I would
be sitting in a room listening to the graceful sweep of
the cloth used for cleaning my weapons rather than
sitting in a room listening to the click of a keyboard.
Perhaps in job of assassin I would have found greater
satisfaction.
I imagine the pay is better.

ordained

the son was a chronic runaway
he smoked pot and drank
a lot

the daughter swallowed pills
and slit her wrists
from side to side

the parents told the people
these children make us miserable
please give us your support

the people told the parents
children are a burden
they take your time away from us

where two or three were gathered
no one ever asked, what's going on inside that house
to make those children flee

Smoked Camel Lights with Michael in law school

Winston Lights the summer I spent with Greg
Marlboro Lights when I was in love with Calum
And Merit Ultra Lights with Steve
I was adoring and attentive with the Camels, Winstons, and Marlboros.
Complained bitterly about the Merit Ultra Lights: "Those are the most disgusting cigarettes on the planet. How can you smoke that crap? When are you going to quit? Is the sound of your oxygen machine going to drown me out when we are in our rocking chairs? Well, if you're going to smoke, can I bum one?"
Twenty-nine years. Steve is still around.

different

for 35 years my family has gone to great lengths to
distinguish me from them
they are extroverts
I am introvert
so they say
proclamations of this different-from-them can be
seen plastered upon my baggage like so many
luggage labels of the world traveler
she's always been an introvert, we are all extroverts
so said, steeped in superiority
well, I suppose if you mean I'm not a loud mouth,
attention-seeking narcissist, then yes,
I am different

the knife

Cadwell told me the one indispensable tool for a
rancher is a knife.
You should get a knife he said.
Here, use my knife he said.
You've not gotten a knife?
Ask Buck or Jones—use one of their knives.
No you cannot borrow my knife.
I'm leaving. Don't call me til you've bought a knife.
Here, I got you a knife. Don't lose it.

And so, I have a knife and it is an indispensable tool.
I use it everyday.
And today I brought Cadwell these flowers, saying,
Look Cadwell, I used my knife! I cut these for you!
He shook his head.
He huffed at me.
He took the flowers
and smiled.

rainbow lakes

We hiked all day
As I squatted and my urine soaked the ground
I wondered

Am I symbiotic with the earth

The gash on my arm from a branch
The spider bite on my ankle

Or am I a foreign being

Desiccating her
No less than a pipeline, a wind field
A toxin

unsettled

we sit in the sun reading
I feel like standing up and walking away
walking away into the woods
down to the stream
walking away and never turning back
there is the blue jay my father loved
and my grandmother's cardinal
it is dangerous to think anything of them being here
those birds being here in this moment
it is useless to think it is a sign
to conject meaning from these birds
the cardinal sits in the bush tweeting
I have to remind myself it is not speaking to me
it is tweeting at another bird
if it flew to me and landed on my shoulder and
whispered in my ear that would be a sign
but of what?
one year:
two screenplays
three grad school applications
four clients
eight (of eight) successful motions
162 blog posts and nothing to do but sit
the sun is warm the breeze is cool
the sky is cloudless the birds tweet
my hair is too long money is too short
the blue jay and cardinal have concluded their
conversation and are off
they have places to be

just sit and look pretty

only a handful of people noticed she was missing
that was why he kept her so long
but she had become a liability
she'd become expensive
she was bleeding all the time
he didn't mind that
it didn't stop his needs being fulfilled
she was just complaining all the time
I'm in pain
I don't feel well
she would probably say
he'd not cared for her properly
she would probably say
she needed medical attention
it was enough he provided for her
he shouldn't have to pay her deductible as well
she was broken
she couldn't be repaired for a reasonable price
the best thing to do was discard her
reduce reuse recycle
her useful life had ended—meaning
she was no longer useful to him
but she would not go to waste
he didn't believe in waste
the pigs get fat and the hogs get slaughtered
her organs and entrails would go to the pigs
the rest he could use for his fire
besides there was another
there was always another

she was so weak it took only one blow to end her
why didn't she duck? why didn't she run?
she had always been weak, he thought
that's why it was so easy to manipulate her
too easy
she wasn't even a challenge
he used the axe he bought for her
a reminder—she was always costing him money
he used the axe he bought for her to chop the wood
he used to warm his house
it was the least she could do, he thought
it was easiest to split them at the joints
wrists then elbows, shoulders, ankles, knees
he dragged her pelvis onto the tree stump
she used for splitting his wood
he laughed
splitting his wood
she'd been good at that
chop your own wood warm yourself twice
he couldn't resist one last time
he parted her vulva and slid his penis into her vagina
feeling the reassuring bump of her cervix
he preferred the proper terms for things
words like rape, assault, abuse were so vulgar
how could he rape her?
he provided for her
he paid for the roof and the walls that protected her
he paid for the food that nourished her
he slid himself in and out
in and out
feeling that sweet release

from campsite #5
we all make choices #2

I met a man
he demeaned me
and then?
I stayed

I dated the man
who actively purposefully destroyed my career
and then?
I stayed

I lived with the man
who tried to tear my family apart
and then?
I stayed

I moved out on the man
who abused me everyday
and then?
I moved back and I stayed

I dedicated my life to the man
who tried to kill me
and still and still
and still I stayed

I chose it over and over and over
and then?

I chose to leave
and now?

my family
united

myself
alive

my soul
restored

my will
iron

my choice?
stands

Mercy

Today I had a fantastic day of writing and now I would like to take a hot bath for it is chilly and the wind is cutting through me. A hot bath would be a small reward for a good day of work but there are no rewards (but the work itself).

We are either inside or outside. Inside is in the Jeep. Outside is in the elements. 12 hours in. 12 hours out. Sleep: inside. Eat, hike, work: outside. This is our life.

Duke is presently sleeping on his cot. He is a trooper. He deserves a couch. I made the choices that got us here. That brought us to this. That brought us here: to campsite 23. I chose a man who hated me and I let him take my life.

I chose him and my people scattered. Still. Duke is beside me. Through it all, he has been beside me. Where is his mercy?

the waves of ballycastle

cottonwood wearing october yellow
thank you hazards from a passing truck
unexpected favorite song
joy keeps rushing in

nuzzle from a friendly dog
warm greeting from a friend
smile from the corner-store clerk
joy keeps rushing in

chocolate crinkle christmas cookies
blue sky dotted with white
laughter of a little girl
joy keeps rushing in

no matter what you do to me
no matter the things you say
hold me down or beat me up
joy will keep rushing in

"Everyone I love dies."
"Aye, they do. An yer left livin'. It's not fair."
"I love you Paddy."
"Aye. An I ain't afraid a that."

leaving

Uncle Joe died a year ago. I wasn't there. I didn't attend my Uncle's funeral because I was lying in a hospital bed with staph.

"Fighting for her life" is how the cable news channels reported it.

"Lieutenant Mary Walker fighting for her life as she battles an infection related to the injuries inflicted by Mijares Al Abassi the Taliban leader Lieutenant Walker killed when she single-handedly rescued four American soldiers."

Three. I rescued three soldiers. In my book you have to be alive to be rescued. In anyone's book actually. If you are alive you are rescued. If you are dead you are recovered. I rescued three. Recovered one. Michael.

Michael O'Conner's body was recovered at the scene. He might have been rescued but for my bullet and because of that, two years earlier the news channels referred to me as "embroiled."

"Lieutenant Mary Walker embroiled in a fight to clear her record and her name after a friendly fire incident left Sergeant Michael O'Conner dead."

It made better headlines to change the lead. America craved a hero and the Army needs recruits so rather than vilify me for shooting Michael through the head the Army focused on the positive. I'd single-handedly rescued four American soldiers and killed one high-value target and seven of his soldiers. Mary

Walker was no longer embroiled. Mary Walker was a hero.

Pay attention American boys, American girls: You can be a hero too. They paraded us around until July 4th. Us = me + the rescued three. Just as I was plugging—as scripted—the wonderful care I'd received from the VA hospitals and doctors I collapsed in front of the morning-show-watchers of America.

On August 15th I was waiting for death (rather than fighting for life) at Walter Reed while Uncle Joe lie down to rest for the last time under the Cottonwood by the stream that runs through Walker Valley. His friends toasted his life, poured bourbon on his grave, and went back to work.

Me. They said I would have been redeployed but for the staph infection. I think it was the PTSD diagnosis that finalized the paperwork that magically transformed this soldier back into a civilian. I'd put in my time so they let me retire. I left the Army with two medals, a diagnosis, and a service dog: an appendage trained to "help" me.

Lane. "Right-hand Lane" is her Christian name. A rescue. Found in traffic. Hence. . . . Taken in and trained by folks that give their time, their talent, for folk like me. She is good (at times over-zealous) at keeping track of me. I suspect that in her eyes I am not as well trained as she because I do not trend toward following the rules. Rules. WTF. I don't want to be in this game. Never wanted to be in this game.

She's a nice dog and all but the fact of the matter is, three years after the event and I'm still jumpy as shit. Three years later and if you seem like a threat to me I might take you out. That is what they tell me. Lane is supposed to stop me from taking your head off by "redirecting my attention" away from the stimuli that may or may not be inducing a trance that turns me into a potential killer. I don't know about that.

What I do know is that to my fellow Americans I am either a villain or a hero and there is no room for gray. If only people would listen to the truth. But the truth is longer than a soundbite: more characters than a tweet.

I know that most days I'm pissed off, panicked, and guilt-ridden. Some days I'm just pissed off.

That daytime TV lady would tell me to start a happy journal—no—a thankful journal. If you believed what she was selling I would start a thankful journal and my life would miraculously turn out wonderfully and I would write a memoir and go on talk-shows and pitch that Kool-aid to another empty shell. I could tell the audience how grateful I am to God. That my thankful journal turned it all around. 'Gosh, God and my journal just made everything better.' But I can't write a memoir because I don't have a happy ending and I think God's an asshole and you can't say that on Ellen.

I know this: The Army doesn't tell you that when you land in Afghanistan you have to unzip your soul and pour it on to the ground.

It is impossible to retrieve something lost among so many grains of sand.

The ranch. We didn't expect snow. Me + Lane = We. Since Lane and I joined forces, so to speak, my language has changed from me to we.

We didn't expect snow in August. But it came and after we turned off of SR 352 and began the final ten dirt-road miles to the ranch, I didn't think we would make it. After all that has happened to die frozen in my Forester because I was stupid and didn't think about snow in Wyoming.

I didn't think snow + dirt road = 4WD truck. But we pulled through. Lane + Me + Forester = We. We arrived and then we stood on the porch of the cabin that has housed four generations of Walkers. Lane + Me = We. We stood on the porch.

Lane sat. I stood on the porch contemplating the door. She waited patiently. I contemplated the door which is the strangest thing. I don't understand the reluctance to pass through a doorway. It doesn't make sense to me. I didn't enter a building to be confronted by the enemy. I wasn't trapped beneath rubble after the bomb blasted.

It was a quiet evening in Afghanistan. I'd just gone to watch the sunset. It all happened in the great vast emptiness of the desert. Why should I be reluctant to go inside? It is counter-intuitive. I would think inside would feel safe. But it isn't that. It isn't being inside. It is going inside. Crossing the threshold.

I know there is no one inside the cabin. I know it. But there is little chance I will cross the threshold and enter the cabin. Lane + Me + three body-sized duffle bags on the porch. Me. Staring at the door.

I feel silly. But I do it because I know it has to be done and we can't stand here on the porch until we freeze to death. Mary did something stupid. She stood on the porch for no good reason and they froze to death. Not the duffles–just she and the dog.

So I open the door and Lane does the sweep. For all I know she is sitting just out of sight counting to 100 before returning to me to signal that all is well: the dwelling is safe. But she takes her job seriously and what she is actually doing is checking every room, every inch of the cabin.

On her return to the porch she will sit at my feet and bark once if it is safe to enter. If it is not safe to enter Lane will exit the dwelling and lead me a safe distance away.

Every time. Every building. Every dwelling. She has always barked once. I feel silly but we do it and then we enter.

For so long unknown and yet so familiar sweet memories and grief wash over me as I enter the cabin. Wood burning in the stove, baking bread, his welcoming embrace. His bear-hug floods my memory. The Carhartt coveralls and coat hanging by the door hold his form, emitting the musky scents of cattle, cut hay, diesel, and earth.

It is comforting to feel sadness, not anger. To see happy memories, not horror. To hear the far off tinkling laughter of a small girl and the boisterous voice of the man charged with her care for a dozen summers.

The house is spotlessly clean. It looks as if Uncle Joe has just stepped out to go to town for a meeting of the Liar's Club. It looks as if any moment he will walk back through the door.

On the kitchen counter there is a paper grocery sack containing coffee, bread, butter, jam, eggs, and bacon. A pile of neatly stacked wood stands next to the stove. A 4x6 card with instructions: propane, electricity, water. Hank's signature. The scent of Allure hangs in the air, evocative of happy times.

All is quiet. The busting activity of the working ranch is gone. Cattle, chickens, horses. The passing goat, sheep, dairy cow for whatever 4-H ribbon I was pursuing. Men working, neighbors visiting. Mrs. Cadwell teaching me to plant and then harvest and put up fruits and vegetables from the small but productive garden. Silent.

My room. The room of an industrious, successful, stable teen going off to college: West Point. It wasn't Yale or Harvard, Princeton or Columbia but, "it'll do," said Uncle Joe. "Certainly, by the time you graduate the Army will let women be snipers. After they see you shoot, how could they not?"

Bits and pieces added through the years: a new quilt, an overstuffed chair, a milking stool as ottoman, a wall hanging, framed photos.

Dragging the duffle bags into my room it is the photos that attract my attention: a very small Mary on the now ancient tractor; me and Annie and her Bloodhound Luke; standing on the podium at the Olympics with my gold medal and my big smile; West Point graduation; me and Uncle Joe showing off vegetables from the garden. "They tell the story of my life," I said to Lane as she sat on the bed watching me.

Uncle Joe's bedroom. His watch on his bedside table. His shaving mug and brush by his sink. In his closet, starched and ironed plaid shirts, jeans. Khakis for dressier occasions. His suit is gone. I guess he took it with him.

I looked into his top right drawer hoping to find his secret stash of cigarettes but there was instead a box. Inside: my Olympic Medal, Silver Star, Purple Heart. When you reach the point that you just want to throw them into the ocean your shrink suggests you mail them to a trusted friend or relative. I did and here they are. The box contains the letter the Army delivered notifying Uncle Joe of my injuries, vis-à-vis, "she's not dead." The invitation to the Silver Star ceremony. A photo of me and Michael: two young officers eager to defend our country. Eager to make our families proud.

"Look Lane. This is Michael. Come up on the bed. Let's lie down. I used to sneak into this bed when it stormed. There was a tree. One of the branches scraped along the roof when it stormed. It spooked me so I would slide out of my bed and run in here as fast as I could and sneak into his bed. Uncle Joe would pretend not to notice, pretend to be asleep. He would turn on his side, his face away from me, and

I would snuggle up, sort of burrow into his back, and I felt safe and warm. . .protected."
LOVED.

The man. The rattle of a diesel engine, of metal scraping woke us. Lane and I went to the kitchen window and looked out. A pick-up with a plow attached was clearing the space between the cabin and the barn. The Forester was just about buried. The driver of the truck deftly avoided it as he pushed snow into a giant mound at the far end of the lot where it would melt into the holding pond. How does he know? He's done this before?

"He is plowing the lot," I say to Lane. "The lot. That's what we call that big open space between the cabin the barn and the shed. When they sort the cattle for sale big semis pull in there and turn around to wait to be loaded to take the cattle away." Lane is always interested in what I have to say, or at least she pretends, but in this moment she is mesmerized by the truck.

The color (red) and the size of the truck are off-putting. Sure you're a rancher but do you need a 2-inch lift and 35-inch tires? You must be overcompensating. But when the truck stopped and the man alighted—oh my.

Lane smiled and wagged her tail. She was glad for company. I was not. This company, striding across the lot, was all boots and jeans, belt buckle and tucked-in flannel. Plaid. Rolled sleeves revealed the large rough hands of a working man and the ribbing of a thermal. The shirt stretched across a broad chest and strong shoulders. He was hatless and sans jacket against the wind which only made him more rugged looking. He pushed his sandy-brown hair off his forehead as he strode up to the porch.

"Oh Lane. That looks like trouble." It was too late. We couldn't hide in the bedroom or creep down to the cellar and pretend we weren't home. We were standing in the kitchen window gaping at him.

I hadn't looked at a man—as a man—in years. Classmate. Colleague. Brother-in-arms. I was unaccustomed to the satisfying discomfort of meeting a man I found attractive. There was no time to check myself in the mirror. He was standing on the porch, waving at us. Marlboro Man was going to get: me. Rumpled clothes, messy hair, sans make-up: me. We did the only thing we could do. Lane and I went to the door and opened it. We stared until he spoke:

"Hi there. I'm your tenant. Reed McLeod."

"My tenant?"

"Your uncle leases me the homestead. I've been running cattle on that side of the ranch for five years or so. Moved into the house 'bout 18 months ago."

"He never said…"

"Thought I might dig out that car so I can finish the lot. Mind if I go in the barn, get a shovel?"

Tenant? Five years? House? How do I not know?

Bark! Bark!

"Sure."

Reed McLeod turned and walked out to the barn Lane prancing at his heels. Half-way to the barn he stopped, dropped to one knee, and they shook. A very polite paw-in-palm greeting. He read her collar and I could hear him saying, "Hello Lane, I'm Reed. Wanna help?" To which Lane barked. She barked her happy "Yes!" bark.

Yes! I want to go in the car.

Yes! I'd like a biscuit.

Yes! It's safe to go inside.

But this wasn't "Yes, Mary" this was "Yes, Reed you handsome devil I'll follow you anywhere." Lane, my loyal service dog. Gone off with the first man to turn her eye.

I unearthed hat, gloves, boots and went out to help. I might not be a glittering conversationalist but I am a soldier. I can dig. People don't have to talk to dig. Makes you winded. Slows you down. Turns out Reed never dug a trench in the Army.

"I've been looking after the place. Keeping things up, repaired. Figured you'd be back. Didn't want you coming home to rubble."

"Thanks."

Lane occupied herself sniffing around then pouncing on the snow drifts, sticking her head in up to her neck, then pulling her head out, shaking the snow off, and starting again.

"She's hunting mice. Dogs can hear them under the snow. It's a popular pastime with dogs around here."

"Oh. Interesting."

"Glad I came by. Hank said you text, were on your way. I thought you probably got held up when they closed 80. You must have made good time. This will probably melt, knock wood, but I figured, just take a few minutes to clear a path so you can get in and then I get here and here you are!"

"It's ten miles from the road."

"Well there I got lucky. The county plow, Andy's the day driver, you'll meet him, was headed back to town as I was turning in and he took that first ten miles. Those trucks go like a house-a-fire. I could barely keep up."

"They do that? Clear the road to the ranch?"

"Nope. That was just pure luck that we passed each other and he had the time. We'll clear a spot out at the asphalt for your car when winter comes then you can use the snow-cat to get out to the road. Course sometimes winter catches everyone unprepared. Even Hank was cussing about this. She said hasn't been a snowfall like this, in August, in a decade. Maybe two, she said. But, like I said, this will probably melt and we won't get good and snowed in until October, late September at the earliest. Hank leave you a list? Last year she gave me a provisions list. So I don't starve she said. Heck, I have to go to town anyway. Hell, high water, or snow! I gotta go."

Reed laughed at his rhyme then asked me for the key to the car. Instead of handing it over I got in, started it up, and backed across the lot, parking it well out of the way of his plowing operation. I got out and stood by the car holding Lane by the collar until he finished.

Alighting his vehicle, Reed surveyed his work and looked proud. "You can probably park your car in the shed. You'll want to drive the truck anyway. The road will be bumpy as the dickens after this snow melts."

"That old thing?" I pointed to Uncle Joe's beloved Ford.

"1972. Best year for Fords. Never needed a new one since," Uncle Joe said this when anyone got on him about that old truck.

"No. That's a good farm truck. Thing runs like a top for feeding and stuff but you'll want to go to town in the blue one. Here. Help me."

Reed walked to the equipment shed and pulled on one door. I pulled the other and I swear I heard an announcer saying, "Mary Walker you just won a brand new truck!" Reed was as excited as a little kid.

"They match. Except for the color and the lift. I added the lift to mine. Don't want to be sucking up water going across that creek. Check it out! Keys are in the visor or, well, maybe the cup holder, check the cup holder. We bought them at the same time. Got a heck of a deal. Practically two for one. Joe said, 'come on with me, we'll steal those trucks.' He was a character. I sure miss him."

Reed paused. A shadow of grief crossed his face. My building frustration at my Uncle having such a close friend and keeping it from me evaporated. If this man and Uncle Joe were close, well then, I knew that Reed McLeod was kind.

Uncle Joe was the kindest man I've ever known. He would give you the shirt off his back but if you had a mean bone in your body—if you treated folks badly he wouldn't give you the time of day. "I don't have the temperament for it. It hurts my heart Mary. I'm simple. I just want people to be nice, be kind to one another. Not that hard to do, right?" His words echoed in my memory as I studied Reed. His face, like my Uncle's, was kind, yes, but with a sadness there. Uncle Joe carried a heavy heart, I wondered if Reed did too. I wondered if that was the foundation of their bond.

Reed looked at me looking at him, then jumped slightly as if he just remembered something.

"Well, you're all set. Here's my card."

"Reed's Automotive. You're a mechanic?"

"You need anything, just call."

"Quality service. Anytime—Anywhere."

"See ya later."

And he was off. Unfortunately, watching Reed walk away was as stimulating as watching him walk toward us. No one ought to be that overtly sexy. He even turned and looked over his shoulder, then waved as he got into his truck. Would it end? It was raw, kind of … shattering. I asked Lane, "What do you think Uncle Joe was thinking when he leased the homestead to that tall drink of water?"

Bark. Wag. Smile.

"Just because you like him doesn't mean I have to. He's awfully … chatty."

Bark!

"You hungry? I'm hungry."

I pushed the equipment shed doors closed. The truck unnerved me. Uncle Joe never bought anything new. He kept everything. Repaired everything. His sheets were darned and patched for crying out loud. A new truck? A fancy new going-to-town truck. It wasn't right.

And that Reed. That was a problem. Not the man, it was nice to feel like a girl for a few minutes. Really nice, actually. But. I could do without the snow removal. With the snow I had a barrier. Protection from peering eyes, well-meaning neighbors. With the road plowed, anyone could drive right on in. It's the country. Country folk to my recollection come right on in. Don't even knock just holler some version of "yoo-hoo, anyone home?" I pictured them bringing casseroles and pies and wanting to stay and visit.

They didn't. Weeks passed. The snow melted. The temperature roared up into the 70's. Not one soul came to visit.

The Dream. It's always the same and it comes with startling clarity. Not emotional or cognitive clarity. I mean it is vivid. Crystal clear. Like HDTV there is an almost other worldly sharpness to the images. There. The dream always ends there: at the moment, at the second I looked down and saw blood and a hole. There was a hole in my shoulder. I looked at Smitty, packing my shoulder with gauze, and asked, "How did that happen?" I don't remember anything after that.

They say I drove back to base. Three men who were relatively unharmed–physically unharmed–were in the Jeep and it was I who drove back to base. I drove back to base with a bullet in my shoulder and my innards slowly pushing through a gash across my stomach.

They say they told me to stop. They say they tried to get me to stop to change drivers but I wouldn't. They say I screamed "a primal scream" and so they just packed my wounds with gauze and then shirts and finally wrapped a pair of pants around my midsection to try to hold everything in and I drove back to base screaming and bleeding out and they prayed for my continuing consciousness. They prayed that I wouldn't pass out, crash, and kill us all. The Fog of War. That's why.

That's why they say I can't remember. The Fog of War. A trance-like state induced by trauma during which you might do heroic acts like carry a man twice your weight through a burning jungle flooded with Napalm or you might do unthinkable acts like shooting your best friend through the head.

They say you should talk about it. The PTSD shrinks say you should talk about it. I DON'T WANT TO TALK ABOUT IT. Why can't my fog start when the sun glints off my scope? Why can't it all just blank out from that point? I had to watch the goddamn sunset. That's why they didn't want us out there, messing around, "training" for sniper school. Because when the sun goes down a beam of light can reflect off your scope, you idiot!

STUPID. STUPID. I WAS STUPID.

I was lucky that son-of-a-bitch Mijares Al Asshole was out there. Otherwise I could have been that soldier that shot up a bunch of people in the desert and caused a fucking international incident. I DON'T WANT TO TALK ABOUT IT.

But they gave me that goddamn medal and paraded us around and all we did was talk about it. The scripted version. Stick to the script Mary. CNN, FOX, Ellen, MSNBC, NPR, even Dr. Oz. WTF! But not that black lady who owns her own TV channel. Not her show. To her it was all about how a white soldier (me) shot a black soldier (O'Conner) through the head.

Michael O'Conner was black. I can't change that. Michael O'Conner was my dearest, closest friend. I won't change that. We went through West Point together. We always had each other's backs. My bullet went through Michael's brain. I wish I could change that.

That black lady won't let me on her show because I shot a black man through the head.

Talk about your trauma. Talk about how you killed Mijares Al Abassi—a high value target. Talk about how you single handedly rescued four soldiers. Talk about all the shit you don't want to talk about but I'm not supposed to talk about the black lady barring me from her show. I'm not even supposed to know about that.

Well fuck them.

And fuck her.

And fuck you.

I DIDN'T KILL MICHAEL!

"Good. That's the first time you've said that. Very good." Quiet, understated, matter of fact. That's how she said it, my PTSD shrink. She didn't even flinch when I slammed her potted plant against the wall.

She just said, "Good. If it takes 'the black lady' to get you to state the truth, well, I'm glad she turned you down. This 'black lady' has helped deliver your first breakthrough, Mary. Can you say it again? Can you say, 'I didn't kill Michael O'Conner?'"

"No."

"Why not?"

"Fuck."

Michael. Somewhere between Michael's last inhale and Michael's last exhale my bullet passed through his brain.

The autopsy showed that was all that was left of Michael: his shallow in and out breath. Everything else was gone. Organs shut down to maintain life. Everything shuts down to protect the heart and the breath that are essential to life.

Without breath there is no life and I took that. I took his last breath. He didn't decide, his body didn't decide, God didn't decide, I did. The autopsy showed his death was imminent. What I did made no difference in Michael's outcome. It didn't matter. But it matters.

They want you to maintain this persistent state of cognitive dissonance.

FACT: Michael was breathing when my bullet went through his brain.

FACT: I didn't kill Michael O'Conner.

If I didn't kill Michael why do I feel like a murderer?

Last week I told my friend Jules: "I think I've reached the anger part of my grieving process. I think I'm going to be angry for a while." She replied,
"It's not like being angry ever helped anyone. You just need to be more positive."
I broke Jules' nose. And as she looked–incredulously–at the blood running down her starched white shirt I said: "I feel <u>positive</u> that could have been worse. 'I didn't die today.' Write that in your happy journal."
That afternoon I bought a Subaru Forester (why not a truck?!). I packed my belongings and my service dog and now I'm here.

Where it is quiet.
Where I can't hurt anyone.

I've had my coffee. Lane is fed and watered and wee'd. The lot and drive have been plowed. Now. I am going to fill the tub and sink slowly and deeply into a hot bath.

And drink bourbon and smoke.

You wonder why they stay

My daughter cried. She sobbed. She screamed. She shook. Snot ran down her mouth to her chest. She made no move to wipe it away. We had pulled into an overgrown field. Corn stalks high enough to camouflage the car. I couldn't risk being found and questioned by the police. It was quiet. A bit spooky. But nothing imagined in this field could be worse than our reality. If the State learned we were living in my car, my kids would certainly be taken and given to their father. The State reasons that an alcoholic abuser in a house is better than a loving mother in a car.

I couldn't take the crying. I told her if she didn't stop, I would leave her. I turned off the car. I told them to put the seats back and lie down. It was time to sleep. We needed to sleep. I needed to sleep. My daughter stood in the front seat bouncing with distress. Her fists clenched. Crying. She was not going to lay down. She was not going to sleep. "Lay down or I will leave you here! Lay down and be quiet!" Her small body shook as she fought against the fears she could not articulate. She could not calm herself.

I became enraged. I got out of the car. I walked around to the passenger side, lifted her from the seat, placed her in front of the car. I closed the passenger door, walked around to the driver side, got in, turned the car on, and backed out. She stood among the corn stalks, framed in the headlights. Crying. She stood alone in the field crying as her mother backed out the car and drove away.

I drove a short distance along the gravel and stopped. I got out of the car, walked into the field, and collected my daughter.

In that moment I'd become him. I was no better than him.

I will never know what that did to her.

ELLIE

With Paddy's very specific instructions zipped into the front breast pocket of his anorak Jackie readied his boat for the trip to Scotland. He was to select a young Border Collie to replace old Drum who after sixteen years of service laid down for his final rest. Per Paddy's instructions the new dog was to be a female and strictly and most assuredly not a puppy. "She's got to be fully trained but young. No more than eighteen months," Paddy shouted as he tossed the mooring ropes up to Jackie's sure and steady grasp.

"She'll be expensive if she's trained. Why not train her yerself? Ye've got the time."
"I'm too old to be messing around with that."
"Too bad old Ted Hope's gone. He'd give you a run. He trained up til the day he died."
"Just give Brendan the list, Jackie, an bring me back my dog."
"Alright da. No need to be fussing."

The initial stretch of the trip to Gare Loch could be treacherous. The waters off Rathlin where the North Atlantic Ocean and the Irish Sea meet are at once passionate, angry, formidable, awe-inspiring, and always dangerous. Sailors operate with reverence for these waters. Jackie sails these waters daily but never takes his experience for granted.

Out of Rathlin Sound, Jackie turned North into the Firth of Clyde, then passed Arran on toward Millport. Here, the character of the trip changed entirely. From Millport to Garelochhead was 25 miles of wonder. Jackie thought he ought to some day drive up the A78 rather than sail alongside it. He could stop to trek through the deep woods, visit pubs in tiny towns steeped in tradition, and explore castles that dotted the shore. Jackie didn't often wish for company but this particular stretch of earth was one to share.

Mooring at Garelochhead, his boat secured, Jackie's host collected him.

"Brendan Kerr. You're Jackie, yes?"

"Yes. Standing in for my father Paddy Doyle of Rathlin."

"I know your father. He is a fine trainer. Drum was a champion."

"He was a loyal dog. Worked until he died. Was he one of yours?"

"Aye. A bit surprised Paddy didn't retire him. Sheep are hard work."

"There's not much herding on Rathlin. So long as they don't fall into the sea, find their way to the pub, or board the ferry, there's not much place for sheep to go."

"Suspect old Drum was good company for your da."

"I'd say that's true."

"Coffee?" Brendan asked as arrived at the farm.

"I don't mind," said Jackie.

"Come in. You can gaze a bit at the wee ones and then we'll go out to the kennels."

The man busied himself with kettle and mugs. "Milk?" Jackie assented. Milk was splashed in on the coffee powder, steaming water poured over. Jackie accepted the proffered mug and tarnished spoon. He walked through the barn gazing at the puppies. Each litter was in a different stage of development from one very rowdy bunch nearly ready to go out to the kennels to a pile of wiggling fur nursing at their mother. "What's that black spot there?" Jackie indicated the undulating mass of black and white interrupted by an inky black smudge.

"The neighbor's Newfoundland. There was an accident. Only that pup survived. We hoped the pup would take but she's a wee one. Doesn't have the strength."
"Have you a bottle?" Jackie cut him off. "I mean, if you don't mind."
Brendan pulled a wooden box from under the work bench. A bottle was fished out and handed over.
"Suit yourself. There is some dried milk replacer on the shelf. Best I can do at the minute." Then, sizing up the volunteer said, "you sure?"

Jackie followed Brendan's gaze to his hands. A person could be forgiven for thinking Jackie's large hands, scarred from physical labor, were good only for brutish tasks but Jackie's years as a fisherman made his fingers nimble.

When he cared for Katherine she taught him to knit saying, "If you're just going to sit there you might as well be productive," and he became very proficient over the two years it took his mother to die. So prolific a knitter was he that ten years on every resident of the Island possessed and wore a Katherine Boyd jumper. Jackie designed the whimsical pattern in honor of his mother's joyful spirit.

Then too, there were his father's sheep. The lambs that needed nursing were assigned to young Jackie when he lived at home and brought over in a wagon when Jackie had a home of his own. So it wasn't the rough worn paws of a native from the most rugged island in the Northern Hemisphere that picked up the puppy. These were the loving capable hands of a gentle man who'd spent his life caring for others.

Brendan returned to his work saying, "I'll leave you to it then. Come on up to the house when you're finished."

As they settled into a corner of the barn, Jackie rested the puppy on his chest. He thought that if the wee girl could hear his quiet breathing, the steady rhythm of his heart, if she could feel his warmth, smell the scents of sea air and sheep carried on his jumper she would be comforted.

In this swaddled place he offered her a few drips of warm milk. She opened her mouth, took in the nipple, clamped, and began sucking. Having been told she wasn't taking, her vigor and enthusiasm surprised Jackie and he relaxed, enjoying the comforting sounds and smells of the farm.

A few days prior, the wee one had been plucked from the protection and warmth of her family and placed in the midst of a wiggly and aggressive clan. They were puppies, like her, but to the wee girl these animals were strange. Their long hair got in her nose and poked at her eyes. There was a lot of pushing and shoving to get to the milk.

She wanted to curl up with her mother and go to sleep. She wanted her brothers and sisters. She was in a big clump of warm fur with breathing and heartbeats but it was unfamiliar. The breathing was staccato, irregular, not the relaxed harmonious rhythm of her family. These hearts beat quickly. The heartbeats of her brothers and sisters had been slow, measured. This family smelled different, not earthy and nutty but pungent, sweet. She felt desperately lonely.

In Jackie's embrace the pup felt protected. He was large, like her mother. The cadence of his breathing matched hers. Their relaxed heartbeats thumped along together. He moved at a familiar languid pace. In his arms she felt peace. Relieved of the burden of fighting for sustenance she drank as much as she could and soon, with her belly full, her body warmed, and her soul assured, she slept.

Jackie took up residence in the barn, feeding the pup every few hours, building her strength. Taking pity on him, Brendan offered Jackie a cot and insisted he share meals at the family table. In return Jackie plucked Brendan's to-do list from the cork-board in the kitchen and set to checking off those tasks that were perpetually moved down in favor of more pressing items:

- ✓ re-shingle the small shed
- ✓ white-wash the chicken house
- ✓ tune-up the kids bikes
- ✓ patch the old rowboat

In the wakeful hours of the night Jackie sat under the stars and knit Brendan's wife a sweater with yarn swiped from her *bag of good intentions*: knitting set aside after the birth of her fourth child in as many years.

When the time came that the wee girl was strong enough to make the journey home, Brendan fitted a box together. His children provided a blanket for her travels.

Brendan wondered about Jackie. What motivated this man? What did he have or not have at home that he could abandon? What sort of life did he lead that he would just put it on pause to nurse an orphan puppy? A puppy so small, even if she lived she would never amount to much. Brendan didn't think she would be fit to breed. She would certainly never be a working animal.

Brendan didn't ask. He was familiar enough with the vagrancies and challenges of life. What motivated a man was his own private business. Six weeks after collecting him, Brendan drove the man and pup back to the shore where Jackie's boat was tethered. The men shook hands, Jackie boarded, readied his boat, secured his charge, and sailed south for Rathlin oblivious to the storm that await him.

"I couldn't just leave her to die!"

It was the sentence that finally unleashed the flood of unspoken resentment. After mooring his boat in the harbor, Jackie carried the pup in her box to Cullen's to introduce her to the residents.

When he placed the box-with-puppy on the bar Paddy launched in with, "what the hell is that?" Followed directly with, "where is my dog?"

Jackie tried to explain but Paddy was not having it. Each attempted sentence was interrupted with another question, an accusation, a slight, an insult, until Jackie exploded shouting, "I couldn't just leave her to die!"

Jackie's feeling that Paddy had left his wife, Jackie's mother, to die alone was thrown up between them. Paddy's belief that Jackie had come between Paddy and his dying wife bubbled up from under his collar.

Dying was their business. A private affair between husband and wife. It was not the place for a child to interfere. After a few moments of glaring silence Paddy turned on his heel and walked away.

The residents went back to their pints. They weren't fazed by the exchange. Paddy and Jackie were the only two on the Island who hadn't discussed the bad feelings between them. There was a sense of relief. Now maybe the two men could move on from their anger and grieve the death of the woman they loved.

Maura was glad when the argument subsided, because now she could turn her attention to the adorable puppy: paws at the top of the box, head peeking over, hind feet searching for something to step on, to push against, to hoist herself over and out. Maura helped, taking the black ball of fur into her arms and nuzzling her face inhaling the earthy nutty scent of Newfoundland.

Point of fact, if Cullen's stood across the Sound in Ballycastle Maura would have had a strict "no dogs" policy. "But I don't live in Ballycastle" she would sigh, explaining to a hapless tourist with a muddy snout resting on his lap, "my pub is here, on Rathlin, where for over 200 years sheep farmers have had working dogs and those dogs have found their way into this pub."

Truth was, never more than a handful of dogs lived on the Island at one time. But one muddy snout, one spray of wet-dog scented water onto a newly purchased isle-knit was enough to ruin an entire holiday, so part of Maura's schtick with the tourists was to fein exasperation with the dogs and shrug her shoulders with an "it's beyond my control" expression.

But this little one. This baby peering up at Maura. This little girl kissing Maura's nose with her tiny pink tongue. She was a dream. Maura's maternal feelings, which she believed had died with her son, roared to life and she promptly and certainly christened the little girl "Ellie."

"Lady Eleanor if she's ever for tea with the Queen, otherwise, Ellie." Maura said this with such authority and finality that no one questioned her pronouncement. Ellie she was and Ellie she would be.

A month before her first birthday, Jackie took Ellie to see the Newfoundlands from the Italian School of Canine Lifeguards. Watching the demonstration from Ballycastle Beach Ellie was impressed with their extraordinary skills. Far from shore the giant black dogs jumped off speedboats, leapt off jet-skis, and dropped from helicopters. They hauled people in by lifejackets or by having the "victim" hold onto their harnesses.

Ellie was astounded when as a finale "Mac" pulled a rubber boat filled with nine of his canine colleagues from far out in the water all the way onto the shore. Ellie weighed eight stone at her last check-up so she imagined nine of her would be a lot to tug.

They were admirable animals no doubt and Ellie enjoyed the show enormously but as impressed as she was with the dogs' abilities she was even more enamored with their form-fitting rescue harnesses. So captivated was she that Jackie obtained the name of the manufacturer and, following specific instructions as to how and where to measure the still growing puppy, ordered a custom-made, very expensive life jacket. Ellie waited anxiously for weeks while it was sewn and shipped, visiting Bronagh daily at the post office.

Bronagh finally announced that the anticipated box had been delivered! Ellie and Jackie opened it, secured the vest around her midsection, and rejoiced when the sleek jacket fit perfectly. Unlike her previous life vest, adapted from an old human one, this didn't ride up to her chin when she sat down or rub against her legs when she swam. She adored the colors of the jacket: black and blue with strips of silver reflective tape. She thought it made her look like a seal effortlessly slicing through the water.

Sometimes, as they got close to the harbor Jackie would let Ellie leap off the boat and swim to shore. She would swim across the cove, climb out at the beach, and then walk down the road to meet him at their truck. After seeing the Italians, each time she did this Ellie imagined she was rescuing a distressed swimmer.

It was from this practice that Ellie and the seals got to know one another and these friendships were why Ellie often snuck off to go swimming in the cove. She didn't understand Jackie's concern about her habit of cavorting with marine mammals. Certainly, thought Ellie, I am much more like a seal than a sheep, a Border Collie, a Kittiwake, or a cat. These were the choices for animal companionship on Rathlin. Ellie had a working relationship with the sheep, the Border Collies were haughty, the Kittiwakes were bad-tempered, and the cats were, well, cats.

The last Saturday in September, as Jackie readied his boat for the monthly supply run to Belfast he heard a familiar voice.

"You shouldn't spoil her."
"Oh yeah, how's that?"
"It's not good for her to be at sea all day. Swimming with the seals, hanging out at the pub, waiting at the Post to collect her mail."
"You're a storehouse of information."
"She's too smart to be hanging around on a boat all day with the likes of you."
"I am sure there is a compliment for someone somewhere in all that."
"I sent you to get me a dog. Over a year ago. I've been herding them sheep myself."

Jackie couldn't help chuckling to himself. His da walked by Jackie's cottage every morning with his sheep. Those sheep were getting a whole lot of extra exercise to accomplish this but the stubborn old man was hell bent on making sure that at dawn each day the sheep bell rang and hooves echoed on the paved road that passed by Jackie's cottage.

Jackie didn't let on that he'd changed bedrooms. He'd taken to sleeping in the room on the opposite side of the house and since then wasn't bothered by the sounds of Paddy and his sheep. Still, he couldn't help think what a hassle it was for the sheep.

Paddy didn't let on that for the past year, every Monday, Wednesday, and Saturday, when Maura was supposedly dog-sitting Ellie, he'd been training the giant Newfoundland to herd. Now here he was, fit to be tied. Jackie was taking Ellie with him. Paddy needed her. He wanted to take her to the sheep trials in Ballycastle. Paddy adjusted his cap, shoved his hands in the pockets of his Carhartt (his only weakness being American goods), and kicked imaginary dirt.

"What is it your wantin' da?"
"That dog of yers."
Jackie silently counted to five before responding.
"What about her?"
"I'm wantin' her. That's what. I'm wantin' her to spend the day with me. She's been lookin' forward to it."
"How's that?"
"Could I just keep her while yer away in Belfast? Is that askin' too much?"
"Why would you be wantin' that?"
"You gonna make me work for this Jackie?"
"You gonna keep walkin' past my place at dawn?"
"Is it a trade you're lookin' for?"

The argument might have lasted the day had Maura not interrupted, "What are you two going on about? Jackie, leave the poor girl with Paddy, she's been looking forward to the sheep trials for a month. Paddy, quit waking the earth with your early morning treks around the Island. No reason those sheep need to be traipsing around at sun-up. Now, Jackie, are we ready?"

In her beautiful way of cutting to the heart of a matter, Maura had spoken and it would be done. Ellie trotted down the gangplank toward Paddy, passing Maura as she trudged up. Jackie helped Maura onto his boat, Paddy tossed up the mooring ropes, and each went his way. By sun-down Ellie had her first trophy.

American in Paris, Texan in Marseille

She had a wonderful time and he was hard to read.
Collected her in Marseille, was good natured about dropping the Australian she'd met in Frankfurt at his respective accommodation.
Over then to Aix and the grand little hotel, she could never remember the name.
Two singles or one double? One double.
Day before the race.
She was meeting Jacques at 16:00.
They left their cases in the room and went out for a walk and to get a bite to eat.
Back to the room. She collected her things and went to meet Jacques. He didn't show up so at half-four she went to the Internet café to check email. No email from Jacques.
Back to the room. She borrowed the runner's mobile phone. She placed a call to Jacques who agreed to meet her later. When? She didn't know. She never did understand a word he said.
The runner was sitting in bed, resting, having had a bath and a cuppa.
She flopped down on the bed beside him. They chatted a bit, kissed a bit, and engaged in the first bit of sex of the visit. Nice, quiet, clean, lovely.
Jacques phoned. He was ten minutes away. She dressed and went downstairs to meet him. She brought him a bottle of wine.
"I've given up the drink, but my wife will love it."

They talked about the project. He agreed she should work on the risky project. It would be dangerous. There was no way they could guarantee her safety. "What was life without excitement?" she thought.

They agreed to meet again when she returned to Paris and parted amicably.

Back to the room. A shower. She and the runner went to dinner. Italian. Very nice. Puffed pastry filled with goat cheese and spices. Delightful. Pasta with mushrooms in cream sauce for him. Cesar salad for her. No alcohol. The marathoner was on deck.

A short walk. Back to the room. To sleep.

She wore long sleeved, long panted pajamas trying to create an atmosphere of sleeping, not sex. It was game-time and he needed to have his head in it. A hug. A kiss. And the edge of the bed. Facing away from him, she clung to the sheets. 03:00 the revelers returned. Making home of the hallway as revelers do. Both awake. The obligatory snuggle. A quick kiss. Back to the edge of the bed.

Race day.

He ate. Rested. And dressed.

She dressed, stretched a bit and walked him down to the start. She felt good. Strong. Ready.

Back to the room. Three hours to wait. Exercise. 75 reps for chest, delts, tris, bis, abs, quads, glutes, hamstrings, and calves. Shower. Grab camera, jacket, and cash for her. Carbs and protein for him. Down to the line. 11:40. Wait. Clap, cheer, encourage. Wait. Chat, banter with the blokes on the curb. Wait. Engage. Fantasize.

"Do you know someone in the marathon?" asks the Brit standing on her right.

"My boyfriend is running today."

She lies. It is France, after all. Everyone is in a romance. And it was a nice lie, anyway.

"Oh, did he come all the way from the states?"

"No. He's from Marseille. I'm just over." She lied again. An American living in Paris. It was cliché. Better always to claim you're on holiday.

It was a nice lie. An American on holiday having a romance in France. She was rather enjoying herself. Wait. More banter, more cheers. The Brit, a B&B owner, left the scene. She cheers. She waits. She talks to the guy on her other side. This time she doesn't lie. It is not nearly as interesting. As for him, he's married and waiting on the wife. They joke about the runners coming in who look fresh, like they've just stepped off the bus from around the corner. They wait. They loudly encourage those slogging along. She waits. 12:22. The runner rounds. Clearly, not off the bus. She cheers. He passes. She turns and runs up the alley to meet him at the finish. Her thrill for him surprises her. She decides to go with it.

She doesn't realize she is at the edge of the slippery slope. The one she'd careened down so many times before. In France it is even more treacherous. The slick Paris streets, the dark narrow alleys of Aix, the sea at Marseille. All rife with hazards.

She takes photos of the runner. She congratulates him. She is genuinely enthusiastic.

Back to the room. She draws him a bath. She goes after a sandwich for him. Bathed and fed, he's back into bed. She lies beside him. He's sore. She rubs his legs, his arms, his chest, his back. Sex. Nice, light, quiet. Shower. Dress. Champagne. Chocolate. Kissing. Supper. Mediterranean. Fried goat's cheese. Sinful. Three dips: chopped olive, hummus, and cucumber-yogurt. Couscous and vegetables for him. Greek salad for her. Wine. Good conversation. Coffee. A short walk. Back to the room.

To Bed. She tries to keep a respectable distance. She is losing her footing. She feels his distance. She wants to deny it. It is there. The presence is strong. It keeps her awake. She can feel herself slipping.

She can't sleep. She is thinking impetuous thoughts.

She flees to the toilet and writes.

She sits on the toilet at 3 a.m. peeing, typing, and brushing her teeth. He taps at the door.

"What are you doing?"

"Multi-tasking."

"Well, write away then. Come back to bed soon."

But he doesn't really come to the door.

She writes into the night.

She writes about a girl who falls in and out of love her whole life. Always a different time, different place, a different man.

Do you believe in love at first sight?

Yes.

Her love was like a stay dog. When it came around it needed you desperately. It was glad to see you and grateful for your every deed. But it loved you too hard and needed you too desperately and no one can return the longing of a wasted dog. She'd wind up restless, pacing, ravenous. What if the next place along the road had a softer bed or better scraps, or let her come inside a bit, out of the cold? What if the next place loved her better?

She wrote of a girl who was destined to repeat her mistakes. Of a girl who lived life fully. Of a girl who found the great passion of her life and it grounded her and made her whole.

She dreamed of being a woman who didn't write in the toilet at three a.m. and she was terrified of not being the woman who wrote in the toilet at three a.m. She stole herself, got a drink of water, and went back to bed.

Breakfast. Coffee, juice, and yogurt for her. Full breakfast and more for him.

Back to the room. Pack. Carry down. Check out. To the car. She is feeling sick. She fears it. It might be coming early. Should she bail? She should bail. But she's downing the slope. Her head has started to take leave and she struggles. She holds on for a moment. And then she's gone. She makes an irrational decision. She'll take it as a sign. If it comes, they are not meant to be together. If it doesn't? Destiny.

Home. His home. Marseille. Just 40 minutes from Aix. He cooked rice and salad and crunchy pressed chicken. Red wine. Chocolate. Nice. Discomfort. She should have stayed in Paris. Sure, she knew he wanted to test the waters. But not without sex. If everything else was terrible, he knew he could count on the sex. They always could with her. It was the one thing she really excelled at. ,

Now she was stuck. In Marseille. Bleeding like stuck pig. Bloated like a dead fish in polluted water. A searing cramp across her back. Raging, screaming, bursting ovaries. She's inadequately prepared. And she has to tell him. About the first part anyway. She would spare him the details.

It isn't destiny. It is not love. It is a sexual relationship. A sex-only relationship. And this of all subjects comes up. She's distressed. She handles it poorly. Her head is trying desperately to come back online. She smokes. She tells him. He handles it better than she. He wanted the sex enough to disregard the rest. A second bottle of wine and a good turn in the sack.

She smoked. She slept. In the morning sex and a lie-in until half eight. Not as long as he'd liked, but she was awake, which would mean she would want to chat, so they might as well get on with the day. He was sore, so they scrapped the planned hike and went off to see Cathedrals and such. A brief stroll on the beach, a wine-soaked lunch, coffee, a turn around the harbor, another coffee. Another bottle of wine. Later, dinner.

Back to his house, his room. She drinks whiskey. He joins her. Things improve. He'd have been better off drinking whiskey earlier in the day. He'd have been better off if she'd started drinking whiskey earlier in the day.

She smoked. He wrapped his arms around her. And that was that. A good hard fuck. An old fashion tussle.

He didn't realize that the simple act of putting his arms around her on the veranda overlooking the sea would transform her. It was the how she was transformed that was sticky. He liked the sex. She excelled at sex. He hated to lose that simply because she liked him. She liked him. That was unacceptable.

His room. Morning. Finally. It was almost over. He raced to get her on the early train. Speeding. Running red lights. Answering for her at the ticket window. She was not, not, not going to miss that train.

He didn't know she was already gone. He wrapped his arms around her. Then he fucked her. So she left. She said goodbye, boarded the train, and didn't look back. Not once.

She sat on the train. As always, worried that she was on the wrong train. But it was the train at Platform 5 and Platform 5 was to Paris. Where else would all those people be going?

Why did he do it? Why did he take her home? What on earth was he thinking? Why did he tell his parents about her? She was flattered and disturbed. Why? Who tells their parents about someone they hardly know?

A good fuck in Paris was really all she had been. So when his mother rang when they were in Aix and asked after her and told him to have her rub his knee. . . It seemed like such a personal statement. If you don't know a girl well. Very well. Never, ever, under any circumstances tell her that your parents know about her. You might as well pour oil down the slope and shove her yourself.

The Paris train was beastly. Hot dry air pumped in on crowded cars. Children and businessmen. Yanks and Swedes. Spaniards and Jordanians. A wandering Scotsman. There, no doubt, to remind her.

It was a glorious four days. Truly. She forgot the rest of the world for a while and was swept away. In his arms? Somewhat. In his smile. In his quiet. In his eyes. In his order and neatness.

Sadly, she was like the Texan she'd seen in Paris at springtime. That poor girl was all wrapped up. In love. She felt passion and beauty and when his arms were around her, she was transported, transformed.

He was cold, disinterested, and aloof. Everyone could see it but her. He was kind and accommodating. She was blind. Wake up girl. We all felt for her. It was humiliating. That poor girl. All of Paris privy to it and none of us could make it stop. None of us could make her see. He was kind and accommodating and generous. The worst offenders of women's hearts always are at the start. The further on the time dragged, the more formal, proper, distant he became.

The runner, noticing that she was behaving like the Texan, was waving the flag. She might have been roping cattle, springing oil wells, and running for president she was so Texan: big, beautiful, and completely out of touch with reality. So he was distant at the train. He said nothing of seeing her again.

Thank God for goodbye. She liked goodbye. She knew goodbye. She effected goodbyes the same way she removed a band-aid. Swift. Final. Out. Like a paratrooper. That was the only way.

She'd asked for a sign. It came in the exact form she requested. Red. She failed to heed it. Did you go in like a lion? Get out. Like a paratrooper. Once you woke to it … if you woke up feeling like a Texan … that was the only appropriate response.

She sat on the train. She licked her wounds.

Traveling North, she dials, hears the familiar ring.

"Hey."

"Hey Violet."

"Wanna cook a turkey? Some cranberry? Some stuffing? An American holiday is apropos my weekend."

"Why?"

"I've been a Texan."

"Oh my. Are you down or out?"

"Out."

"OK. Turkey, peas, potatoes, stuffing. But no cranberry. I hate the cranberry. I'll do it, so long as dinner is followed with an evening of muscular dimwits. Yanks, preferably."

"It suits the theme."

"They follow the rules."

"Je ne sais quoi."

The whistle blows. The train jerks to a stop.

She is happy to be home.

After reading too much David Foster Wallace

Sunday, September 27
Joe Skeen Campground, El Malpais, New Mexico

Duke and I weren't supposed to be here, now. Joe Skeen campground wasn't supposed to happen for another two weeks. Bluewater Lake was scheduled first. We'd come from Phoenix via Flagstaff and it was this trajectory, heading East on 40, that determined the destination. Never mind the fact that we were not supposed to be in New Mexico in the first place.

If you are a person who traces back to pinpoint the moment you made the decision that caused the upturn of events, our presence in New Mexico could be traced back to Ella's suggestion that we go see Mills Canyon.

Or, it could be traced back [all the way] to Wichita to the auto repair place, charged with determining whether the Jeep was road-ready, missing the fact that the alignment was out by more than 25 degrees and that the transfer case was leaking oil. No, not leaking, spewing.

But fundamentally, Duke and I were at Joe Skeen Campground on this date because the free camping at Bluewater Lake was a dump. Carbon dated 1975. We drove through and caught shade from the locals [I felt infinitely more welcome in Juarez when Ella and

I walked across the bridge from El Paso in 2011]. So Duke and I peed and drove back to 40 to drive further East to 117, then South past the El Malpais Ranger Station to Joe Skeen. BLM campground. Free for seven days. The afternoon of Friday, September 25th.

Sunday dawns bloomy, beautiful, as all days seem to begin in New Mexico but it is mere provocation. Duke and I have walked 23 miles since Friday and we are feeling as though we've been here for days and days rather than just 48 hours. The thermometer tells us it is only 84 degrees but the heat is oppressive. In between walks, we sit. I in my chair and Duke on his cot. I have read David Foster Wallace's book of essays *A Supposedly Fun Thing I'll Never Do Again* twice. Except for the nauseating missive on tennis. That, after scanning the first page, I skipped. Twice.

Duke is crushing on a white Shepard-mix named Hildy and he is being such a boy about it. He wants to walk past her campsite 100 times a day. He concocts reasons he needs to go for a walk. He reminds me that he gets up for me ten times a night [at least!] to go to the toilet. And so we walk.

Up the road from Site #1 past the mis-matched couple in Site #2 and on-toward single man with Boy-scout backpack and fishing cap in Site #5 in order to pass Hildy. White Shepard-mix. Site #3. As Duke passes, Hildy, of the privileged | the unleashed, runs out to him excited, as if to say, "Hi Duke! How are you? What are you doing today?"[1]

Duke turns up his collar, lights a cigarette, and as if it is an afterthought—he just happened to pass by | he was going this way anyway—gives her an over-the-shoulder growl and continues on his way. Dejected, Hildy returns to her sympathetic owner who is apologizing to me and calling to her to, "come Hildy!" She returns to Site #3 to wait for the next time Duke deigns to pass her way.

Après our mid-morning excursion past Hildy's and our sentry around the campground, Duke and I ate too much for lunch. The last three slices of cheese went at breakfast. I tore one slice into tiny pieces and placed them strategically around his paper plate [I broke his food-bowl in Payson, Arizona when moving from Site B-3 to Site C-11 to accommodate a Scout-master and his pack] and covered them, the cheese

----

[1] Re: the mis-matched couple in Site #2. The man is older with long gray hair tied into a pony tail with a piece of twine. The woman is younger with a sleek bob haircut which, unaffected by the wind, presents itself as perfectly coiffed. She is smartly outfitted in Garanimals t-shirt and shorts. For those not steeped in media in their formative years, Garanimals is children's clothing that is easy to mix and match. I use the word here in the sense that her clothes fit closely, like children's clothes often fit, and her outfit is perfectly, perhaps too perfectly matched—mechanically matched, which compliments her VP striving to be SVP haircut.

slices | not the scouts, with dog food. Unimpressed by my cunning, Duke enjoyed the cheese | left the dog food.[2]

For myself I placed each of the last two cheese slices on street-taco size corn tortillas then folded the tortilla in half. Last night I was placing one-half slice of cheese on each street taco and giving the other half-slice of cheese to Duke and I thought, "I should melt these in the pan over the stove." The stove being a heavy metal disk screwed to a slender green propane bottle.

The pan. Pan? Pot? I believe it is in actuality a pot or described better still, a sauce pan. The point is, it is high-sided. I should place the tortilla in the sauce pan and then place the cheese on the tortilla and let the cheese melt a bit and then the whole thing will taste cheesy and delicious instead of tasting like dry corn.

The original plan for supper was to heat black beans with Hatch chili salsa then put this mixture on top of the quesadillas. I'd gone over the recipe and the process in my head many times over the course of

---

[2] I have since discovered that if I refer to dog food as "cereal" Duke is less inclined to rebuff it and if it contains a few pieces of sprouted-grain toast slathered with raw-milk butter and sprinkled with biodynamic cinnamon-and-brown-sugar-mixture he will cheerfully ingest a modest amount of the dog food. He disappears the cinnamon-sugar toast like Pinochet dealt with oppositionists.

the day. First, heat the black beans and salsa then dump out onto a plate and set aside. Place the tortilla into the sauce pan [it is the only cooking vessel I have —I'm making do] then the cheese onto the tortilla and heat until cheese is warm and melty. Remove from pan and spoon black bean and salsa mixture over cheesy tortilla, fold, eat like a street taco.

I'd spent the afternoon snacking on chips and pineapple salsa [a good blog post would include the trade names and links]. I'd spent the afternoon snacking on Trader Joe's Board Chips and Trader Joe's Pineapple Salsa so at 5:00 pm making a big dinner seemed like overkill and at 5:05 the sun clears the metal awning and blasts heat like rollers off the big island until the sun sinks below the ridge at 7:00. So cooking—really, doing anything between 5:00 and 7:00 in the evening is in my opinion pointless.

All the other campers have tarps, tent footprints, rain flies, anything that can be strung up with bungee cords to create a barrier against the heat exhaled from the sun and carried through by the wind. The effect of the strung-up windbreaks is that Joe Skeen Campground looks like the slums of India as represented in a Hollywood blockbuster.

In terms of shelter-constructing materials I possessed a small 5'x7' tarp and a ball of green twine. My small motor skills are that of a pre-schooler [a side-effect of being an incubator-baby one has said]. As a result I've never learned to tie a proper knot like a half-hitch or a double fisherman or an alpine butterfly. A square knot [if that is the one composed of twice doing the first motion involved in tying a shoe] and the kind of bow for tying shoes or wrapping presents [at which I am also hopeless] are the sum of my knot-tying abilities.[3]

The elastic nature of the twine and that as a partner in a project like hanging a tarp Duke excels only at sitting on the tarp i.e. holding it down so it won't blow away [lifting the tarp and holding it above one's head requires thumbs] dooms the project to failure. I long for bungee cords, a larger tarp, a step stool, but there is nonetheless a serene quality to my actions in relation to my desire.

Instead of hanging tarp I ate half slices of cheese-in-corn-tortilla. Duke ate slices of cheese al fresco and I was disappointed by the blandness of my dinner but not so moved as to set up the stove—screw the metal plate to the green bottle; set the green bottle on the green plastic holder; and cook—hold a lighted match in the vicinity of the burner; turn the knob; place the sauce pan on the burner; place the tortilla in the sauce pan; lay slice of cheese on tortilla; wait for cheesy-meltiness to occur; fish the concoction out of

[3] On further research I've learned that my square knot is actually a granny knot which is described as a square knot that has been tied incorrectly. E.B. White would be apoplectic at my use of three—three! parentheses.

the deep-sided pan without spilling said cheesy-meltiness.

I balked at the challenge of extracting a hot quesadilla having already burned black a dusting of sugar in an effort to make cinnamon-sugar toast. The process for making cinnamon toast works beautifully until you try to check the bottom of the bread for toastiness or try to remove the finished piece from the pan given a slice of bread is the exact size of the pan give one-eighth of an inch or so. It is thus difficult to remove the toast without tipping it, which of course means that whatever is not stuck-fast to the bread falls onto the hot metal surface of the pan's interior bottom. Making matters worse, it is a sauce pan on loan.

I think about the acrobatics that will now be involved in returning the pan and wish for a Lodge skillet and wonder if they make a six-inch size. Obtaining a Lodge skillet will require the purchase of a new stove as the tall-tippy version of a heating element I now possess [also on loan] will not bear | sustain the weight of a proper pan and a Lodge skillet is most certainly a proper sort of pan.

I have an affection | affliction for the Lodge pan so ardent when I happen upon one on a clearance end-cap and am operating on a limited budget I will eschew all other present purchases to acquire whatever Lodge product is on offer.

Why a Lodge should ever be on clearance is beyond me for the known fact that if you find one buried in silt at the bottom of a lake even if it had been tied to the ankle of an unfortunate mobster all it takes is a good scrubbing, a coating of oil, a seasoning in the oven, and the pan is like new.

One might argue that silt is a good medium for preserving things. Even so, I think the point makes itself. If not, the point is, a Lodge will sustain any trouble short of a nuclear blast and I'd recon if you asked the person who staged the houses in the Nevada desert for the tests—if they used Lodge pans in the kitchens, that person could pull that pan out of their cupboard and show it to you because nuclear fallout be damned no thinking person would leave behind a perfectly useful Lodge pan.

When I folded the whole slice of cheese into the corn-tortilla this morning I was delighted to sense the flavor of cheese on my tongue. It is unlikely that cheese will again find its way into Duke and my shopping basket. As delicious as it was—Tillamook thick sliced sharp cheddar—the heat bled the oil and even though I had the foresight to pack it in a Ziploc [even I could anticipate the trouble traveling with cheese might invite] the amount of water required to scrub out a cheese-oiled cooler [or worse] could be catastrophic as Duke and I carry an allotment of one-half gallon of water per being per day.[4]

I left two ounces of water in the blackened-sugar-bottomed pan—a goodhearted if halfhearted attempted at loosening the mess—and within two hours it was evaporated. The water. Not the blackened sugar. Reminding us of the preciousness of resources, which is why when Duke pushed his dog food around in order to get each tiny piece of cheese this morning then tossed me a glare of disdain as I shoveled in my second and final unmelted cheese tortilla I told him he would not have one bite—not a molecular odor of human food would be lifted by the upwind breeze to his nostrils until every last morsel of dog food was eaten.

1:00 pm
An hour ago Duke and I devoured pinot-noir sausage and black olive pâté. Heretofore I would not touch a black olive. I've learned to like a lot of foods in my adulthood—tomatoes, mushrooms, the dark meat of a chicken—but at 46 years of age I supposed I would go to my grave feeling the churn of bile at the merest whiff of a black olive and now, under the El Malpais sun I am slathering black olive pâté on sausage. Having previously ingested the last of the cheese and

---

[4] A lecture on this amount of water being not nearly enough is unnecessary. I understand the implications just as I would expect an educated or at least a thinking person to understand the limitations that making do intrinsically imposes.

now the final bites of sausage, Duke and I are officially a greasy-food-free family.

This will no doubt inform and reassure the paramedics when they arrive. "There was nothing we could do—did you read what they ate?!"

4:00 pm
I am tired.
Peed at 8-10-12-2-4-6 last night into this morning.
There is no place to rest during the day [unless I doze in my camp chair] so if I don't sleep or my sleep is interrupted, say, by the need to void my bladder, I am screwed sleep-wise. Once the sun lifts over the ridge there is nothing to do but wait for darkness to arrive. The first seven days of this trip I felt like I was losing weight. I don't feel that way now. This may be related to the sausage, pâté, and cheese.[5]

It is coming on the hottest part of the day. Daily we, Duke and I, go for a walk from 5:00-7:00 pm so as to avoid sitting and baking in the sun. Mercifully, when we are walking we occasionally happen upon a patch of shade.

_____

[5] On January 1, 2015 I weighed 181 pounds. From January 1- September 1, 2015 I went to the gym twice-a-day, six days a week. I ate a healthy diet, and on Sept. 1, I weighed 181 pounds. On October 24, after eating cheese, black olive pâté, sausage, baloney on white bread with ketchup, and sitting in a camp chair for seven weeks, I weighed 160.

On our afternoon Hildy-visit and campground sentry we observe that it seems a fair number of people come here, to this campground, to picnic.

Monday, September 28
Joe Skeen Campground, El Malpais, New Mexico
8:45 am

Duke is not feeling well today. He has elected to stay in bed. Not on his cot but in the Jeep. It is clear that the Jeep is for nighttime sleeping and the cot is for daytime sleeping. He knows this and though he is a notoriously late sleeper he has made it clear he is not getting out of bed today. I've hung blankets and stuffed pillows, slipped tea towels over the windows and strung sweaters from the roll-cage to block out the sun. The aforementioned blankets hold open the back doors and DFW's *Supposedly Fun Thing* is wedged in the driver door between the door and the frame, holding open the door so Duke can get some air.

It could be that his tummy aches from the sausage and cheese fest of the past two days.[6] It could be that his paws are sore from hiking over sand, volcanic rock, crushed gravel, those tiny tan stickery burr-like things [burrs?], and of course the ever-everywhere cactus and heat. I've only put his boots on him once

---

[6] Written long-hand that sentence seemed fine. Typed it seems dirty.

in the past three days. I should perhaps be a better guardian of his paws. It could be that his muscles are sore and he is tired of hiking. I've been keeping a schedule of two hour hike in a.m. and two hour hike in p.m. These are not strenuous hikes. On reflection they could not even be termed brisk walks

if that bee comes any closer I am going to kill it with vengeance and without regret

but they are really casual strolls. I however do not wear a fur coat, as Duke does, [my metamorphosis from pale soft skin to tanned leather skin attests to this] nor do I walk barefoot, as Duke does, and these walks may be extracting a toll he cannot directly communicate. It could be, and I suspect it is, that he is tired.

Tired of heat.
Tired of sun.
Tired of bugs.
Tired of camping, of hiking, of my company.[7]

Duke being in the Jeep during the day means only one thing–travel. Duke is only ever in the Jeep during the day because it is time to move from one place to the next and in his stubborn refusal to exit the Jeep

---

[7] October, 2016: I have realized and accepted that Duke is older than I am and tromping around in the woods and in the desert are hard on him and he occasionally appreciates a full day of rest.

and by his plaintive look I believe he just wants to move on. I, too, am ready to be in a climate less extreme but this campground is free for seven days and we are broke.

The numbers don't lie. I have $270.00 cash for camping. This buys us 27 nights in ten-dollar-a-night New Mexico campgrounds. We have 34 days until the end of October which is how far this $270.00 needs to stretch. I also have limited funds for gas which means we can only drive so far. I meant to write that down. How much gas money do I have? I can't check. We haven't had phone service since Flagstaff and there's no WiFi [if that wasn't an obviousity].

I am torn in a should we stay or should we go scenario. We both liked the Sugarite Campground. Raton is a haul from here. We could go to Sugarite from 10-14 days depending how well they keep track. Our last visit was the beginning of September. Do they register these visits in a database? On a spreadsheet? After Sugarite we could go back to Mills Canyon or up to Rock Springs, Wyoming which might take us to the opposite end of the spectrum weather-wise.

It is so very quiet here.

My second cup of instant coffee has gone cold. I wasted water today. I dumped 14 ounces of cold coffee into the fire pit. A travesty when in this dry-environ we are budgeted 64 ounces each per day. It's OK for me. If I drink more than 64 ounces even though I feel parched [not thirsty so much as dry] I pee all night long and then neither Duke nor I are rested which could be another reason Duke has elected to stay in bed: the past three nights he's been awakened 5-6-7 times by me getting up and out to go to the vault toilet.[8]

He, who never leaves my side. He, who has a horror of being left behind. Is not getting up anymore to accompany me. He is effectively over it, this waking up and getting out of the Jeep and walking to the toilet and peeing and going back to hoist ourselves up and into the Jeep to sleep for maybe another two hours before I have to pee again.

Adding to Duke's misery I was keyed up over the moon last night. It is the week of the super moon. Friday and Saturday it was like daylight all night. There is little to no light pollution out here so the sky is spectacular and since there have been no clouds the moon is free to keep everyone awake. As a finale,

---

[8] October, 2016: I have, for sometime now, peed in a cup with screw-on lid when I have to pee during the night. It not only doesn't disturb Duke's sleep, it is a necessity when the temperature drops below freezing.

Sunday was the blood moon eclipse over which I nearly had a breakdown.[9]

9:45 am
Duke is still sleeping. I am trying not to worry while holding the back passenger door of the Jeep open so he can benefit from the cool breeze which will end in approximately 15 minutes. I don't think he has peed in the past 12 hours. I have to pee again so I am meditating on his not having peed. The breeze is mercifully cool this morning and the sky is brushed with pastel clouds just enough to mute the sun.

Maybe not mute, mute is total. Abate? Take the edge off is what I mean. What word means there is just enough cloud cover to take the edge off the heat? DFW would know. DFW would know a 12-letter word that means take the edge off the heat from the sun.

I hope Duke is OK.
I pray he just needs a day of rest.
I worry too much.
I love every permutation | aspect | variation of the sky.

Today's watercolor clouds are one of my favorite versions. The blue is soft. The sky has texture. Gently smudged yet indecisively streaky in some places. A

---

[9] In short. I'd been monitoring the time of the moonrise. On the night of the eclipse, the moon was late. I took it as a personal affront.

veil here, a puff there, this is the sky of my novelistic aspirations. The sky I struggle to describe and fail. All skies with clouds evoke my longing for any artistic talent and the place and the space and the money to explore | develop | exploit that talent.

Fuck you Bukowski, shut up.

Last year I read a lot of romance writers—Gouge, Binchy, Pilcher—for the purpose of analyzing and adapting their style. The point was to learn how to write a romance novel.

I want[ed] to write Rathlin as a novel.
I plan[ned] to write Rathlin as a novel.
I wrote 186 pages of Rathlin: the Novel.
I liked 10 pages of Rathlin: the Novel.

This year I am reading books to make me smarter. This year I am reading books to make me appear smarter. To make me more attractive to an Ivy League MFA program.

Inter alia:
Swann's Way
Madame Bovary
The Trial
The Three Musketeers
Dubliners
One Man's Meat
The art of fiction: and other essays

and of course too much David Foster Wallace as I suppose Ivy League MFA admission committees disgorge at the thought of a DFW-type darkening their doors | illuminating their halls.

Duplicity notwithstanding, I am indeed feeling enriched mentally | mind-wise. That and the cessation, the ceasing, the pause ...

I've stopped writing. I read and I jot things down. I take notes. I write down words I need to look up. I write down words I know but I want to use that I wouldn't otherwise think of using.

I live outdoors. I sleep in the Jeep from dark to dawn but otherwise I am outside. Out-of-doors. In the elements. Presently in heat and sun and wind and sand. I've not opened my computer since September 6. I could write, "I wonder how it is doing? Is it lonely?" and that might be cute but the fact is I don't care.

I've stuffed my Mac in a backpack and stuffed the backpack between the back window and the roll-cage and except to tell you, except for this present writing, I've not thought about it.

If only giving up
coffee | chocolate | cigarettes | whiskey
were so easy.

As a result of the smarty-pants reading I like very few words and fewer sentences in those 10 pages of Rathlin.

It bears explaining that before the writing of the most recent 186 pages, I was writing Rathlin: the Novel and it was going really well. The story was flowing and I was writing so often, so easily, so fluidly I forgot to back-up and my computer crashed and I lost it all and it just has never returned. I lost it in the crash and it never came back.

eh
meh

10:00 am
Five very browned | burned college-age-looking girls just drove past my campsite in an old maroon Subaru. Two in front, three shoulder-to-well-developed-shoulder in the back, the hatch area stuffed with gear. Colorado plates. They were giggling.

Remarkably the breeze is still delightful. A welcome respite from the relentless sun, wind, heat, sand we have come to associate with New Mexico.

explore | develop | exploit

I am not exercising economy with | my | lines.
Strunk would exercise economy. Three times.

Picked a dead fly out of my coffee and just kept drinking. Flies are so distasteful the ants [who scavenge everything] won't even touch the carcass.

Noon.
Sun. Heat. Wind. Sand.
Duke is still asleep in the Jeep.
Must. Do. Something.

It happened. I did something. Tired of the heat. Tired of the wind. Tired of baking in the sun. Tried to hang the tarp to get some relief. Stacked an overturned bucket on top of the dog bed trying to get twine-attached-to-pen over metal awning. Fell. On my right side. Right arm. I fall so fast there is no time for mitigating movements, other than to shift slightly right in the hope I will land on my side rather than smack the back of my head on the pavement. I succeed and I land on my right side. Hard.

Once I've worked it out that I have indeed mitigated the risk, i.e. not hit my head, that I am indeed conscious, a wave of nausea washes over me. I would say I broke out into a sweat but I was already hot. It is true that my skin instantaneously morphed from dry leather to glistening dew.

Lying on the campsite's cement pad, next to the immovable picnic table, hence the stacking of the bed, the bucket, I tried to work out if I am broken, where I am broken, and how badly I am broken.

My arm hurts. The pain is so breathtaking that I wonder if maybe my arm is broken. I sit up and test it. Nothing is protruding. I can feel my skin tightening as the swelling begins. I can move it a tiny bit so it must not be broken. After all, if it was broken I wouldn't be able to move it at all. That is what people always say.

I can say this: any movement of my arm is forced. The range of movement is laughable. I think it is broken. It feels broken. I can't make a fist. I can't turn my wrist. All I can do is keep it at 90 degrees tucked in close. That is the only position that doesn't induce pain so intense I think I might lose consciousness.

Goddamn it. Duke's been telling me all morning we should leave. Why didn't I listen? I didn't listen cause I was so fucking concerned about money. I don't have enough money to last the month. We have to stay at Joe Skeen for seven days. We don't have enough money for paid camping every day this month. We have a plan. We have to stick to it.

Right arm is unusable. After a few minutes it has swollen to approximately twice normal size. It is stuck at 90 degree angle. The size continues to expand rapidly. My arm is now its own entity. Deserving of a zip code kind of entity. Using only my left arm and sucking in oxygen as my right arm seizes with pain I throw everything in to the Jeep and drive. Not to hospital.[10]

Instead, I fill water jugs and beg paracetamol off nice English couple at ranger station. Who, of course, say my arm can't possibly be broken. I can move it a tiny bit and I am standing in front of them, so it must not be broken. After all, I am still functioning. I close all the vents in Jeep but one and run AC full blast aimed at my arm while I drive six hours to Sugarite. Maddie and Tae's *Fly* plays on the radio, telling me to keep on climbing keep on reaching cause I can "learn to fly ... on the way down."

---

[10] I downplayed the injury for months saying, "it is just hurt." But as I told the story of how I hurt it to a man in Boulder and I got to the part where I loaded the Jeep and drove he cut in and said, "to the hospital" and I said, "no, to Sugarite" and he said, "You do realize your arm isn't just bent, it's healing deformed because it is broken. And given that it's been two months since you hurt it, it should not be that swollen and you still can't grip a thing or turn it or straighten it ... you can't open a car door for Christsake, you can't lift a thing above your waist, your muscles are completely emaciated ... notice the curve ... your elbow isn't bent, your arm is curved. You broke your arm."

Four months later my arm is still bent (curved). It aches at night enough to keep me awake and there are many simple tasks my arm will not do—it simply stops—OK. I think I broke it. Fractured it. In three places.

A year after the accident my arm still aches but is much better. It does not, and will probably never, fully straighten at the elbow.

Friday, October 16
Morphy Lake, New Mexico

Stayed at Coyote Creek last night. Not feeling it. Drove to Morphy Lake this morning. Beautiful but high and chilly. See how long we last. Bit of a cloud cover. When the sun is out the temperature feels perfect.

I am reading *Madame Bovary* and craving food today. I bought an eight-inch Lodge pan at the Walmart in Las Vegas. The weight notwithstanding I cook potatoes, onions, and eggs atop the slender green bottle. I crown this concoction with roasted chilies given to me by Frances of the Broken Arrow Motel in Springer. Healthy and massive though the meal was I am distracted thinking about chicken enchiladas, avocado, margaritas, pancakes, syrup, and options.

The option, for example, to be indoors or out.

I live outdoors. I sleep in the Jeep from dark to dawn but otherwise I am outside. Out-of-doors. In the elements. Presently under a grove of pines, swaddled in wool sweater and oversized Workwear coat. I am swaddled | not the pines. It is 33 degrees but the sun is pleasant.

I love most of this. I am unsure for how long I will be doing it. I guess I just have to keep doing it until my

PTSD symptoms abate. Until I am no longer, as Ella described, jumpy as shit.

October 25, 2015
In the Central Library, Wichita, Kansas

Came in off the road for want of electricity, as a rejection of cognitively-challenged fellow travelers, and due to concern that I had contracted hantavirus or plague.

Thought I had been writing good stuff. Needed to get it into the computer. Just needed electricity. Wanted a solar panel but no budget for that.

In retrospect, I should have just moved to an electric site. It is as difficult to find a table, a chair, four walls, and a working outlet in Wichita as it is while camping in New Mexico.

I am not going to mention the fact that the writing that seemed brilliant in the natural elements loses its luster under editorial glare.

explore | develop | exploit | survive

January 20, 2016
Casa Del Mar Hotel, Santa Monica, California[11]

My arm is healing but it is not fully functional. Still bent, still sore, still aches enough to keep me awake at night. Can't lift anything with it or even complete a simple task like open the door of the Jeep but I can write so I write—longhand in cheap spiral notebooks and Duke and I walk. Now with companion, Peanut.

Duke likes hunting like I like writing—it is all he wants to do. In spite of little success he keeps at it all day, day after day. In spite of little success he hunts whatever is available—chipmunks at Rainbow Lake, mice at Sugarite, too many gophers at Eagle Nest, lizards at the bottom of Mills Canyon, frogs at Morphy Lake, squirrels in Kansas, and, like me and writing, Duke doesn't know what he would do if he couldn't.

––––––––––––––––––––

[11] Wait until I tell you the story of how Cicero insisted that it just didn't look like life had treated me badly ... "You look good," he said. "You don't look as though life's been hard. You look really good." Bukowski retorts, "You look good. He means you're fuckable. You're fuckable so everything must be OK." This reverberates in my head as the old guy in the band at the Casa del Mar Hotel bar sings *You Send Me* and I believe for three and a half minutes things could be different.

The Cream

Here is
a table for your computer
a chair for your form
a credenza for your research
a wall for your thoughts
a window for your gaze
six sides to shelter you
and a door for your freedom.

The Churn

There is no quiet place
to think about how to convey
the horror of the tower falling

I want to stand and breathe
to smell the acrid smoke
the jet fuel
the scorched bodies
to hear the crashing on the street
on the metal awning
to watch the firefighters jump in fright
each time one hit

to feel the coming thunder
to feel the thud
to feel each thud as floor falls upon floor
and grows closer

to watch as Kate stands
in the midst of the chaos
as it happens all around her
and everything inside her screams GET OUT!

I stand
I hear it
smell it
feel it
see it through Kate's eyes
stinging from the tiny bits of debris in the air

I stand
close my eyes
and breathe

the men at the table next to me in the coffee shop
feel uncomfortable

I need a quiet place
with a table for my computer
a chair for my form
a credenza for the research
a wall on which to pin my thoughts
a window to gaze out at the sky
to let fresh air in and anxiety out
six sides provide shelter
a door gives me freedom
to walk out and present myself to the sky
as Kate did
to stand in the blown-out window
as John did
to listen and to hear
to tell their story with compassion

The Butter

"Welcome to the Magic Cottage!" Paddy swung the wooden door open with ceremony befitting the opening of Parliament. The heavy door sighed on ancient hinges.

"A wee dab of oil will take care of that. I'll bring the oil can round tomorrow." Paddy wanted everything to be perfect. The squeaky door was not a good start. Embarrassed. He blushed deeply.

Kate's eyes swept the room. The long narrow space glistened. She inhaled the scents of peat, lemon oil, and Ariel. She recalled a commercial for wood cleaner that depicted three old women polishing a church. A wave of calm lapped over her.

"Come in and we'll close the door. I've got the fire here, all ready, I'll just put a match to it." Paddy knelt in front of the hearth once the heart of his family's life. Cooking, bathing, washing clothes, heat source. Size in relation to the cottage? It seemed the fire might be too much.

"I know what yer thinking. This is far too much fire for this wee house. You'll soon learn to manage it. We can bring in an iron stove and vent it out this flue if that suits ye better, but then, a fire is a cheerful companion, to my thinking anyway."

Kate set her bags on the floor and walked to the opposite side of the room. She skimmed the tips of her fingers along a low credenza. Each of five separate doors on the frontispiece opened to reveal a shelf with a wire basket tucked in beneath.

"That was my idea. With no closets to speak of, and figuring you'd probably want a place for your clothes, Caroline said we should bring in an armoire. But I said since you're a writer you'd want a place for your papers and such.

"Me da built it. When me youngest brother started school me mammy suddenly took a great dislike to clutter. I s'pose who could blame her. Five boys in the house and me da, so he built this cupboard. It sit in the hall that run from the kitchen to the barn. We hung our boots and coats and caps opposite and put our jumpers and school books and little treasures in the compartments. Anyway, I thought this was appropriate. You can tuck your bits and pieces away. Don't worry, I added hooks in the bath, Caroline said you'll need someplace to hang your dresses.

"Through that door is the scullery. That big old cooker's been converted so you needn't worry about building a fire to heat it. We've laid in some provisions to get you started. There's a grocer in Ballycastle and of course the monthly run to Belfast.

"Caroline gave me the dickens about all these blankets piled on the bed but I told her ye can always take em off but if ye don't have enough, well you know. That door on the other side of the bed leads to yer bath. You've got to pull on the string to let the water heat up but I s'pose you know that by now, your travels and all."

A large heavy dining table anchored the center of the cottage. Four mismatched chairs lined one side.

"Now don't you worry that we're all expecting to be invited for tea. I didn't know what sort of chair you like to sit in when you work, so each of us brought one so's you can decide for yerself."

Kate was touched by the care and thought they had put into outfitting the cottage and quietly scolded herself for the childish fears she'd spent days concocting. Paddy spent several minutes explaining each of the photos that decorated the mantel and then with a flourish, led her to his final and favorite contribution to the fitting-up.

"You might need to adjust it a bit for yourself. For me, this is just the spot." Paddy demonstrated: settling into the low leather chair that faced the south-east corner window. "When it's just you in a place it's nicer looking out, I think. You've a splendid view from here."

Kate's mind flashed to the upholstered linen chair facing the window that looked out over Spring Street. After John died she'd turned it away from the conversational arrangement they'd shared and sat gazing at the trees. She watched those trees through the seasons willing the leaves not to change and drop, wishing the branches would stay bare, resenting the tiny hope-filled buds that blossomed into pink showy blooms, found comfort in the waxy green leaves, then, stepping into the dappled sunlight, accepted the deep reds when they came in the fall.

Paddy sprung from the chair and encouraged Kate, "Try it!" Kate settled into the worn leather. It was a good chair. Beyond the window lie a small garden bordered by a low stone wall. A caring hand once tended the garden, that was evident, as was the fact that the flowers now looked after themselves. They did so in a riot of color popping up here and there without a care for placement or order. Beyond the garden an emerald green field dotted with sheep slopes down to the harbor. Kate mentally scrawled "Greetings from Ireland" across the window frame.

"I set this table here. Room enough fer a wee cuppa. Caroline had an idea of covering it with a doily or some such thing but I didn't take you for a frilly doily sort. I swiped a coaster from Cullen's in case you worry about rings, spills, or such. I don't worry about that stuff so much myself, being on my own..."

"It's perfect."

Kate placed her hand on his arm and looked up at him with what Paddy had come to think of as 'those eyes' and said, "Paddy. It's perfect." Paddy smiled, looked at his shoes, then donned his cap, went to the door, opened it, and stepped into the twilight.

As she closed the door behind him, Kate noticed the mat on the floor. A row of hooks above it. Upon one of these hooks hung a stiff yellow slicker. She took it down and saw affixed to the inside collar was a name tape. The label read, KATE.

She had been wandering for months, an adventurer on foreign land. She knew not where she was going. She had no home. No return. No plan. Just here, then there. Keep moving. Know no one. Love no one. Cherish no one and no one will die.

In the space of fifteen minutes Paddy had provided a home. A roof over Kate's head, a grand table for her work, a warm bed in which to rest, a place to store her things, and a chair that had been loved. The greatest gift among them all was freedom. Though Paddy had constructed four walls to protect her, Kate felt free. Paddy had recited no rules, no dos and don'ts, no expectations. There were no strings. Simply. Here is a place to call your own, a place for you to be.

she threw a good life after a bad man

He sat on the bed and pressed the sheets against my shoulders. The sheets pinned me against the mattress. He told me he was tired of me being mad at him. That I should just get over this "Company thing." He said more but I could only think of being trapped. Being deprived of oxygen. I couldn't focus. He wanted me to respond but he continued to hold me down pressing me hard against the mattress. I couldn't breathe.

I was certain he wanted me to say something but there wasn't anything left. He'd ripped everything out of me. The only thing keeping me alive was oxygen and now, he was taking that too. I told him I couldn't breathe. He took it as a personal attack. He said I never loved him. He said I couldn't stand him touching me. He said I recoiled when he touched me.

Why is it when men strike you they can't understand why you recoil? Why, when they hold you down, do they say you are weak for struggling? Why, when they force your freedom from your grasp, do they insist you are crazy as you feel around in the dark for the door. He sat back. He reached across the bed and picked up a box. He told me he wanted to give me something.

"I want to give you something. I want you to wear it everyday so you can remember. I love you. Even when I am not here." Then, he kissed me. In that way. That awful messy disgusting way. He covers my face with his big slobbery mouth. The stench of old man. The stench of disrespect. Nothing in that kiss indicates he sees me at all. He said the ring represented love. I saw indicia of ownership. He thinks I am for sale. It wasn't a ring of love. It was another chain. An outward sign that I am property.

Rings are supposed to show that someone is firmly beside you. This ring was another sign that he was standing in front of me. I was not allowed access to the outside and no one was going to be allowed to get close to me. I thought if someone got close to me, they might see me. I was wrong. The longer it went on the more invisible I was to the world. Maybe my pain is so palpable maybe it radiates from me so strongly that no one can get close to me for fear of being hurt themselves. I don't know. I can't think.

I can't breathe.

My arms were pinned between the taut sheet and the mattress. I couldn't put the ring on if I'd wanted to. He was furious. He took my stillness as an insult. He felt I didn't embrace it. I didn't embrace him. He had me trapped. He had me pinned down. What could I do!? With no oxygen I felt the light fading. He snapped the box shut and slammed it on the bedside table. He stood, put on his suit coat, slung his briefcase strap over his shoulder, grabbed his roller bag, and strode out slamming the door behind him.

I eat. A lot. I drink past consciousness everyday. I sleep. For a while I look for a job. I go back to Brazil. I return to the States. Smoking helps. Smoking and pacing and drinking whiskey helps more. Finally, I collapse. I lie on the couch and don't get up. For a year.

There are hints to my condition beyond the black sweats I wear everyday and the blubber growing over them. The hollow darkened places that frame my eyes. The chipped polish on my nails. The unhealed cut on the top of my hand. Overgrown hair, thinning at the ends. A small tear in my sleeve, a ragged cuff, a missing button. Each signifying I gave pieces of myself away.

I feel the wrinkles invade. I feel my face sagging off its bones. My body is getting plumper and older. I am wasting the few good years I have left. The years I could work all day and play all night.

I feel the elasticity in my skin evaporating as I stand staring at the trash. I contemplate its disposal wondering why I can't move. How will I get this trash from here … to there? I know everyone else in the world could pick up this bag and carry it outside and be done taking out the trash in less than three minutes but it is all too heavy.

I write about my experience and think maybe I will turn this into a book. But then I remember how I got here. We are self. If you give your self in service to others they will take it. It is not what they teach you in Sunday school—to give and give and give and give and then, you shall receive. It doesn't work like that out there.

I pray. I beg God to help me. I tell myself, "Get up off your knees. God is not coming. No one is coming to rescue you. You have to save yourself." I keep telling myself this. But. I don't have the strength to get up.

I should write something Potteresk. Something fantastical, dreamy, pretend. If I write about myself, people will say, "another depressed female. Squandered her life. A lost soul."

The choir does not sing songs of sympathy for the women who threw a good life after a bad man. It is so shameful that no one will admit it—admit they did it too. You will be alone. Maligned. And alone.

Oprah would tell me to start a thankful journal. Then I could tell everyone how one morning I woke up and decided to be happy and my life instantly turned around. I could tell everyone how grateful I am to God and my thankful journal. 'Gosh, they just made everything better.' But I think God's an asshole and you can't say that on Oprah.

Memoir of a Day

Sunday
Sugarite Canyon State Park, New Mexico
Duke and I slept until 0730
it is already warm
going to be hot
we go for a short walk and then
retreat to the relative shade of the shelter
flies and bees
the buzzing is constant
Duke preferred the mountains
the trees, shade, cool breezes
chipmunks, squirrels, long hikes, hunting
here we are in the company of lizards
snakes, flies, bees, grasshoppers
he turns and collapses
waits for it to be over
two women are camping in a very shady spot
they've been here before
they know when you pull in at dusk
the deer and the rabbits and the mist seduce you
the women are ancient
seasoned
each sleeps in her own tent after a day spent
chattering and laughing
two young women with four off-leash dogs walk past
I think
we should follow them
they look like they know where they are going
the trail Duke and I took was overgrown

my snake-wary nature rises as the off-leash dogs
romp through the tall grass
thirty minutes later the women and the dogs return
I thought
I should have asked if we could join them
I am always thinking these things too late
always making the wrong decision
at Rainbow Lakes I chose the shady site
it was cold
at Soda Pocket I chose the sunny site
a fantastic view
surrounded by flowers
plagued by heat and incessant buzzing

1100 hrs
the breeze is beginning to warm
so that is good news | a bonus
but it is evidence [shade = cold | sun = hot]
of my proclivity
to make the wrong decision
to do | to say | to choose the wrong thing
confidence comes with a series of successes
when we are loved, we blossom
so written in *For the Love of Cities*
so what am I doing now?
nothing
if you can't do anything right
maybe the best thing to do is
nothing

a yellow butterfly is occupying a purple flower

one of the old ladies was talking about
the power of prayer
I've been praying
Lord God,
Jesus Christ,
Mother Mary,
Dear Hector,
I've moved on to Michael
now there is Michael, the avenger

it has been a cloudless blue sky all morning
now there is one perfect white puffy cloud
Michael?
when I pray to you you show yourself
thunder
wind
this cloud
are you listening?
will you help me?

in spite of all the saints
and so many sinners
praying together
prayer didn't help Joe
they prayed for Joe to live
Joe died
will prayer help me?
I have to pee

the breeze has shifted from east to west
it is glorious
the flowers smell like marijuana
the clouds in the sky
change each time I look down
when my gaze returns to them
they've taken another shape
I hope Michael understands
I don't mean to be flighty
I mean to be | I intend to be
my intention is to be devoted
what is the right amount of prayer
how much is enough
can there be too much
when I watch the clouds they are still
when I look down they change

1120 hrs
shade has reached the table
shade + breeze =
almost cool enough for want of a sweater

1140 hrs
breeze cool enough
to warrant energy exerted to don sweater
clouds coming over the hill behind me
will they provide relief from coming afternoon heat?
still have to pee but Duke sleeps soundly
hate to disturb him

1230 hrs
Duke wakes
we walk

1300 hrs
we live in this dichotomous world
if you are told
you are worthless
if you are told
you are a failure
if you are told these things
even if it is for decades
you are to rebound
you are to transcend
pull up bootstraps
don't complain
don't blame

but if you are told
you are wonderful
you are gifted
if you are told these things
you may point to those persons and say
I am the way I am because of them

I am the way I am because of them

more clouds nice breeze
met a really nice woman from Texas
she is here with a friend
we met at the entrance to the nature trail

she wants to adopt a hound
I should have mentioned Duke
everyone loves Duke and after all
he deserves better than me
but people don't realize his great needs
his long | prolonged | protracted soliloquies
on the subject of car travel
his panic at being left alone
his need to walk for hours everyday
his insistence that you walk him for hours everyday

1415 hrs
reading Kafka: The Trial
New Mexico has the best skies
no wonder Georgia O'Keefe was entranced
tired
keep falling asleep
long for a lounge chair
Duke has been sleeping on the concrete pad all day
I would lie on his bed | lay on his bed
if I weren't so afraid it wouldn't support my weight
if I weren't so afraid it would give way under me
if I weren't so afraid

1450 hrs
I thought this location
looking down into the valley
would be inspiring but I am just tired
cars keep driving around
looking for camping spots?
hard to tell

two families drove the 7 miles of dirt road just to have
a picnic lunch overlooking the valley

Duke is awake
we will go for a walk
Georgia O'Keefe had a house

1600 hrs
walked part of Deer Run Trail
good trail to collect kindling
four years on scars from the fire are evident
are everywhere
are heartbreaking and beautiful

switched to east side of table to stay in shade
breeze still pleasant
shared two slices of Ezekiel bread with Duke
+20 oz of water = 80 oz for day
Kerigold butter is a deeper yellow than Dillons butter
sesame Ezekiel is better toasted
7-grain Ezekiel is OK not toasted
the southwestern soup was good
straight from the can
wish I'd stopped in my Boulder mania to get cheese
and sausage and a bottle of wine

they say if you think good thoughts
they say if you say good words
good will happen

I will drink good wine and write great works

1630 hrs
no sounds but those of nature
and me and Duke
wind flies bees crickets birds
pages turning, pages flapping in the wind
getting up, circling the concrete pad
returning to lie down again
so many cars have traveled up the road today to
traverse the circle only to travel back down again
the quiet is a gift
am I here
because I chose the wrong side
of all the people involved in all the wrong
I am the only one here

Michael, I am here
Michael, here I am

Duke preferred the mountains
the desert is hard on him
the highlight of his day today was hunting a mouse
he is connected to me
otherwise he would have caught it
and felt fulfilled and purposeful

September 11

John told Kate he loved her, took a deep breath, and closed his phone. He thought it would be better if she didn't know. Crawling across the wet floor through the choking black smoke, the group John was with knew. All escape routes had been destroyed. The exits were blocked, the stairways collapsed, the smoke impassible, the heat was rising. The floor was so hot it burned their hands as they crawled. They knew death was coming for them. The discovery of light streaming through a single broken window gave them an option. A choice.

Moments before the smoke cleared revealing the opening, the group had come to the terrible realization that there was no way out. Lives full of promise, opportunity, hope, plans were over. It wasn't going to be cancer or old age that claimed them. They were going to die in a fire. They could only hope the smoke rendered them unconscious before the heat burned through them. Before the flames reached them.

And then. There was light. A single pane of glass had been completely blown away. A rectangular opening remained. It reminded John of the front door of his family home standing open in the summertime the household taking advantage of a rare cool breeze gifted to Manhattan on an August afternoon.

In front of John there stretched an immense blue sky. Behind him a raging fire.

John stood in the window. Several of his colleagues had gone already. Their falls were varied: one simply plunged. One paused, turned, and fell backward. Some clung to the building as long as they could before falling. Most were crying, distressed that they were forced to choose how they would die: by fire or by a fall. Death was certain. Death was imminent. The only question: How are you going to die?

John stood to the side as they went out, one after the other. A woman sat on the floor across from him. She faced away from the windows her back against the glass, her legs stretched out in front of her, her arms limp at her sides. She was shoeless, sobbing. She looked at John, helpless, and cried, "I forgot my phone. It's in my purse." John stepped toward her, leaned down, handed her his, and returned to the open window.

John knew what he was going to do. To his mind, there was no question that leaving through the window was the better choice. John stood looking out at the brilliant day. He breathed deeply in and out letting the oxygen stimulate his senses.

Everything felt new. It felt to John like he was at the start of a great adventure. He felt her take his hand in hers. She was there and with her, he felt safe.

Kate loved to look at the sky—ever changing shapes and personality. She never tired of marveling at clouds and stars and sun and so for the last time John admired the sky seeing it through his wife's eyes. He felt her squeeze his hand. He knew it was time.

He turned his head and looked at the woman standing next to him. The shoeless woman was holding his hand. She looked into his eyes and said, "Will you go with me?" John nodded and squeezed her hand. Then he and the woman took a collective breath, and together, they leapt.

Site #5, Sugarite Canyon State Park, New Mexico

i am here

                    michael—here i am

you are a child of the sky, he said
daughter of black
tucked in with a blanket of stars
daughter of blue
swaddled in a cloud
child of sun and moon
quiet, dependable
evolving, magnificent
come with me, we will fly away
rise-up child, come home

9 780985 471071